INTRODUCTION TO 3-D SPATIAL VISUALIZATION

INTRODUCTION TO 3-D SPATIAL VISUALIZATION

Beverly Gimmestad Baartmans
Department of Mathematical Sciences

Sheryl A. Sorby
Department of Civil and Environmental Engineering

Michigan Technological University
Houghton, Michigan

PRENTICE HALL
ENGLEWOOD CLIFFS, NEW JERSEY 07632

Library of Congress Cataloging-in-Publication Data

Baartmans, Beverly Gimmestad, 1944–
   Introduction to 3-D spatial visualization / Beverly Gimmestad
Baartmans, Sheryl Ann Sorby.
      p. cm.
   Includes bibliographical references and index.
   ISBN 0-13-191610-6
   1. Engineering graphics. 2. Visualization. I. Sorby, Sheryl
Ann, 1959–   . II. Title.
T357.D310   1996
804.2--de28   95-13664
                                   CIP

Acquisitions editor: Linda Ratts Engleman
Buyer: Donna Sullivan
Cover design: Bruce Kenselaar
Editorial Assistant: Naomi Goldman

Partial support for this work was provided by the National Science Foundation's
Division of Undergraduate Education through grant DUE-#9254207.

The author and publisher of this book have used their best efforts in preparing this book. These efforts include the
development, research, and testing of the theories and programs to determine their effectiveness. The author and publisher
make no warranty of any kind, expressed or implied, with regard to these programs or the documentation contained in this
book. The author and publisher shall not be liable in any event for incidental or consequential damages in connection with,
or arising out of, the furnishing, performance, or use of these programs.

Printed in the United States of America

10 9 8 7 6 5 4 3 2 1

ISBN 0-13-191610-6

Prentice Hall International (UK) Limited, London
Prentice-Hall of Australia Pty. Limited, Sidney
Prentice-Hall Canada Inc., Toronto
Prentice-Hall Hispanoamericana, S.A., Mexico
Prentice-Hall of India Private Limited, New Delhi
Prentice-Hall of Japan, Inc., Tokyo
Simon & Schuster Asia Pte. Ltd., Singapore
Editora Prentice-Hall de Brasil, Ltda., Rio de Janeiro

To our parents, who encouraged us to pursue the careers of our choice:
Paul and Blanche Beyreuther
Jack and Mariam Sorby

Contents

Preface

To the Student: This text is specifically designed to help first-year engineering majors develop their 3-D spatial skills prior to their design graphics courses. But it is believed that the background provided by this text will benefit students in a wide variety of their courses (geometry, calculus, geology, organic chemistry, crystallography, surveying, architecture, and astronomy—to name a few). Answers to selected exercises appear in Appendix I of the text. Special dot and grid paper will be needed for working many of the homework exercises. Masters for this paper are located in Appendix II.

To the Instructor: This text was designed for use in a three-credit course taught over a 10-week quarter, where 2 hours each week are spent in lecture and 2 hours each week are spent in a computer laboratory. However, if you are teaching on a semester system, the text should contain enough material for a two-credit course taught over a 15-week period. There is an accompanying computer lab manual designed for use with I-DEAS software. Supplies that will be needed for effective teaching of the course include 2-cm snap (or linker) cubes, glue sticks, Miras (optional), rulers, scissors, and construction paper. A videotape titled *Hypercubes: Projections and Slicing* is interesting to show when covering cross sections. It is available for rent (or purchase) from the International Film Bureau, 332 South Michigan Avenue, Chicago, IL 60604. An instructor's resource manual is available which includes such things as a syllabus, overhead masters, paper supplies, activity sheets, sample tests, and a complete solutions manual. The authors would appreciate and welcome any suggestions you have for the improvement of this text.

Acknowledgments

We would like to thank the National Science Foundation (DUE-#9254207) for its financial support of this project. Without its support, this text and the accompanying computer lab manual might never have been written. Although this project was NSF funded and was written during a time when the authors were employed by Michigan Technological University, the views expressed in this text are solely those of the authors and do not necessarily represent the views of NSF nor of Michigan Tech.

We would also like to thank the following talented people who assisted us in preparing this text. Kim Ullman and Virgil Schlorke, engineering students at Michigan Tech, drew many of the complicated figures of this text and solutions manual using I-DEAS software. This task was at times challenging and kept them at the computer many hours. Keri Ellis, a scientific and technical communications major, was responsible for the editing of this text. Using FrameMaker software, she also word-processed the text and drew some of the simpler figures. Without her help, this text would not read as smoothly as it does. We would also like to thank our colleagues—Al Baartmans (mathematics) and Lee Erlebach (mathematics) for critiquing certain sections of the text, Dallas Bates (chemistry), John Jaszczak (physics), and Bruce Mork (electrical engineering) for providing applications from their fields. Last of all, we would like to thank our families and close friends for their support during this project.

Beverly Baartmans
Sheryl Sorby

INTRODUCTION TO 3-D SPATIAL VISUALIZATION

1

Introduction to Spatial Visualization Ability

1.1 IMPORTANCE OF SPATIAL VISUALIZATION ABILITY

Spatial visualization ability is vital to success in a variety of career areas. Below are illustrations of how certain career areas rely on spatial visualization ability.

Engineers typically use drawings as a primary means of communicating with each other and with manufacturers, so it is important that engineers be able to visualize parts from drawings. For example, a mechanical engineer must be able to create and understand drawings that represent 3-dimensional objects, like the vise base shown in Figure 1.1.1.

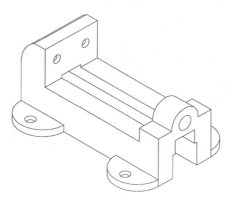

Figure 1.1.1

An architect must be able to visualize and draw buildings and their cross-sectional views. Figure 1.1.2 shows the community house and chapel being planned by the monks of the Society of Saint John near Eagle Harbor in the Upper Peninsula of Michigan.

Figure 1.1.2   Proposed Community House and Chapel, Society of St. John, Eagle Harbor, Michigan. Architects: Page Onge, AIA; and Barry Polzin, AIA. U. P. Engineers and Architects, Inc.

Figure 1.1.3 shows a cross-sectional view of the chapel on the right-hand side of the building. Drawings such as these are used to convey what the final building project will look like from different perspectives. They are then used by contractors in the construction of the final building.

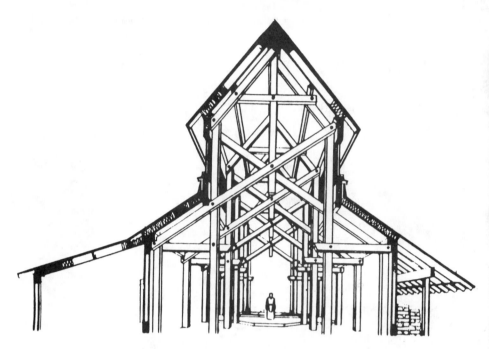

Figure 1.1.3   Proposed community house and chapel, Society of St. John, Eagle Harbor, Michigan. Architects: Page Onge, AIA; and Barry Polzin, AIA. U. P. Engineers and Architects, Inc.

Chemists, geologists, metallurgists, microbiologists, and medical researchers are all interested in the molecular structure of materials. Shown in Figure 1.1.4 is the molecular structure for calcium titanate, a type of ceramic. The three views shown here represent different spatial orientations of the same molecule. The geometry of a crystalline material affects how it interacts with other materials; how it packs to form a crystal lattice; and the strength, elasticity, viscosity, and ductility versus brittleness of the material.

Molecule from 1 0 0 view   Molecule from 1 1 0 view   Molecule from 1 1 1 view

Figure 1.1.4

A mathematician must be able to visualize a planar region being rotated about an axis to make a solid of revolution. Figure 1.1.5 shows the region bounded by the curve $x = \sqrt{y}$ (the branch of the graph of $y = x^2$ where $x \geq 0$), the horizontal line $y = 9$, and the vertical line $x = 0$ being rotated about the Y-axis to form a solid paraboloid.

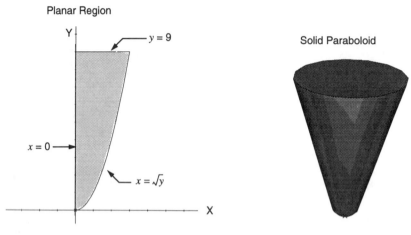

Planar Region

Solid Paraboloid

Figure 1.1.5

Visualization skills are also important for sheet metal workers. Figure 1.1.6 shows a typical transition piece from one size duct to another. Below the transition piece is the larger size duct and above it the smaller size duct. The figure also shows a flat-pattern development of the transition piece. Using this pattern, a sheet metal worker would cut out a piece of sheet metal to that shape and size, scribe lines in the metal, and fold it into the 3-dimensional transition piece.

A surgeon must be able to identify an internal organ by its special shape despite the distraction of many differently shaped organs near it. For example, when performing an appendectomy, a surgeon must be able to distinguish the appendix from the surrounding organs by its size and shape. Similarly, an astronomer must be able to recognize a pattern of stars such as the Big Dipper, despite the distraction of nearby stars.

Although these examples are not an exhaustive list, it should be apparent that some kind of spatial ability is needed to be successful in a variety of careers. The purpose of this text is to provide instruction and activities that will help students develop their 3-dimensional spatial abilities.

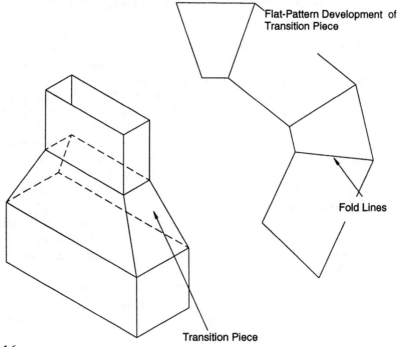

Flat-Pattern Development of
Transition Piece

Fold Lines

Transition Piece

Figure 1.1.6

EXERCISES 1.1

1. Describe how spatial visualization skills would be useful to a dentist? A plumber? A pilot? An artist? A furniture mover? A logger? A quarterback?
2. Name five different career areas that you think would require little 3-dimensional spatial ability?

1.2 DEVELOPING SPATIAL VISUALIZATION ABILITY

Specific training in spatial visualization has not traditionally been a required part of our educational programs. It is believed that play with construction toys such as Legos™, blocks, Tinker Toys™, Erector Sets™, and Lincoln Logs™ can help children develop spatial visualization skills. Experience in physical sports and play with video and computer games are also thought to be beneficial. In research conducted at Michigan Technological University (Gimmestad), a relationship was found between the amount of experience that high school students had in courses such as shop, drafting, and solid geometry and their scores on a 3-dimensional spatial visualization test on entering college. Despite the collective positive effect that these play activities and high school experiences can have on the development of one's spatial visualization ability, there is little *guarantee* that students will participate in enough of these activities or experiences to develop their spatial visualization ability before college.

It is well documented that spatial visualization skills are teachable (Brinkman; Battista, Grayson, and Talsma; Lappan). However, in the same sense that one learns to count before one tries to add numbers, there is a natural order to how one develops spatial visualization ability.

According to Piagetian theory (Bishop), individuals progress through three stages in their spatial visualization development. Individuals acquire sequentially topological spatial ability, projective spatial ability, and Euclidean spatial ability. Bishop (p. 20) claims that "in their early years,... children first discover topological relationships—that is, an object's closeness to other things, its order in a group, and its isolation or enclosure by a larger environment. They further discover that if a figure is folded or stretched, its topological properties do not change." The second type of spatial ability to develop is projective representation: the ability to conceive what an object will look like from a different perspective. If the materials being used to represent the object are familiar, most junior high school students are able to correctly represent different viewpoints of the object. If the materials are unfamiliar or if there is a new feature such as motion, high school students and even college students frequently find projective representation difficult. In the final stage of spatial visualization development, an individual learns to conserve, measure, and otherwise manipulate the Euclidean notions of distance, area, volume, translation, rotation, and reflection. Here an individual combines measurement and projective abilities. Little testing of spatial visualization is done at this final stage; most testing is done at the first two stages of development.

EXERCISES 1.2

1. What activities in your background may have assisted you in the development of your spatial visualization skills?
2. Name two activities at each stage of the three Piagetian stages of spatial visualization development.
3. Why do you think there are few tests for the highest stage of spatial visualization development?

1.3 TESTING SPATIAL VISUALIZATION ABILITY

Tests designed to measure spatial ability at the first Piagetian stage of development will be referred to as low-level spatial ability tests. Such tests require the visualization of 2-dimensional configurations. The Minnesota Paper Form Board Test (Likert) and the Group Embedded Figures Test (Oltman, Raskin, and Witkin) are examples of low-level spatial tests. The Minnesota Paper Form Board (MPFB) Test measures the ability of students to integrate visual stimuli into a pattern. Figure 1.3.1 is a sample problem from the MPFB.* The examinees are required to select the alternative that correctly shows how the parts given in the top left-hand corner fit together. (The correct answer for the problem shown is A.)

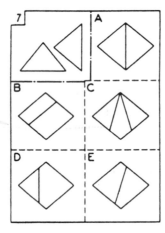

Figure 1.3.1

The Group Embedded Figures (GEF) Test measures an individual's ability to hold a visual *gestalt* (or form) in spite of distracting elements. Figure 1.3.2 is a sample problem from the GEF.† The simple form labeled "Y" to the left is hidden within the more complex figure beside it. The examinees are required to find the simple form in the complex figure and trace over the lines of the complex figure. The simple form is the same size, is the same proportion, and faces in the same direction within the complex figure as when it appears alone.

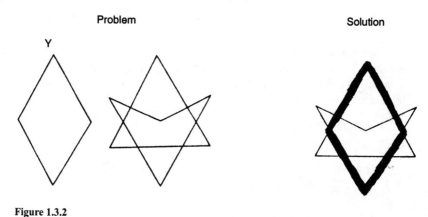

Figure 1.3.2

Tests that are designed to measure spatial visualization at the second Piagetian stage of development will be called high-level spatial ability tests. Figure 1.3.3 contains a sample problem from the Spatial Relations Subtest of the Differential Aptitude Test‡ (Bennett, Seashore, and Wesman). The task is to choose the correct 3-dimensional object that would result from folding the 2-dimensional pattern shown at the left. (The correct answer to the problem shown is C.)

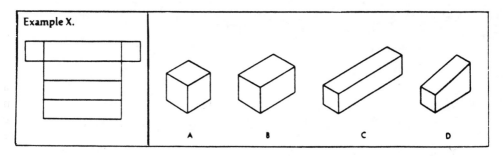

Figure 1.3.3

‡ Reproduced by permission from the Differential Aptitude Tests, Forms S & T. Copyright 1947, 1948, 1972 by The Psychological Corporation. All rights reserved.

    Figure 1.3.4 shows a sample problem from the Purdue Spatial Visualization Test: Rotations** (Guay). In this test, the objective is to study how the object in the top line of the question is rotated, and then picture what the object shown in the middle line of the question looks like when it is rotated in exactly the same manner. The correct answer is then selected from one of the five drawings on the third line. (The correct answer to the problem shown is B.)

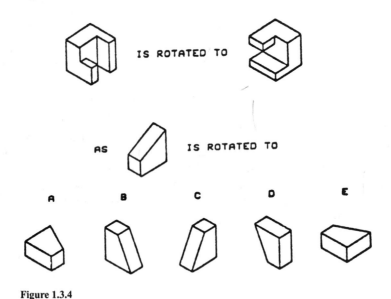

Figure 1.3.4

EXERCISES 1.3

In Exercises 1 to 4, select from the five pictures (A, B, C, D, or E) the one that shows how the parts found in the upper-left-hand corner fit together correctly.

1.

2.

3.

4.

In Exercises 5 to 8, trace each complex shape, and then shade the specified simple form within the complex shape. The simple form must be the same size and face in the same direction as the original simple form.

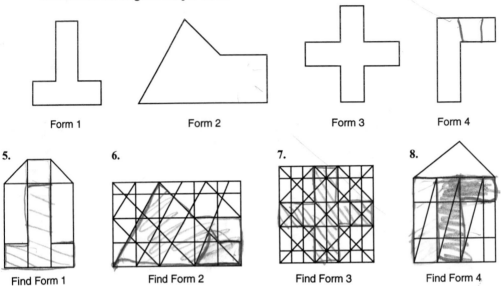

Form 1   Form 2   Form 3   Form 4

5.   6.   7.   8.

Find Form 1   Find Form 2   Find Form 3   Find Form 4

In Exercises 9 and 10, choose the correct 3-dimensional cube (A, B, C, or D) that would result from folding the 2-dimensional pattern at the left.

9.

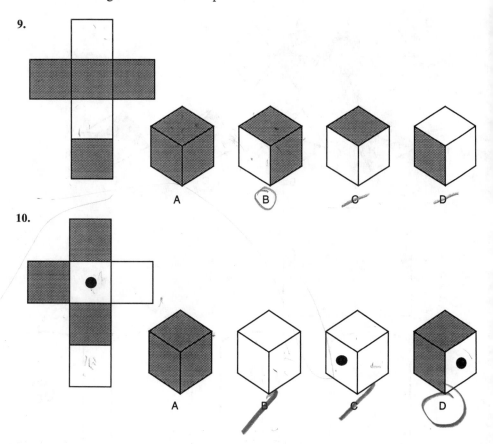

10.

A   B   C   D

In Exercises 11 and 12, choose the correct 3-dimensional object (A, B, C, or D) that would result from folding the 2-dimensional pattern at the top.

11.

12.

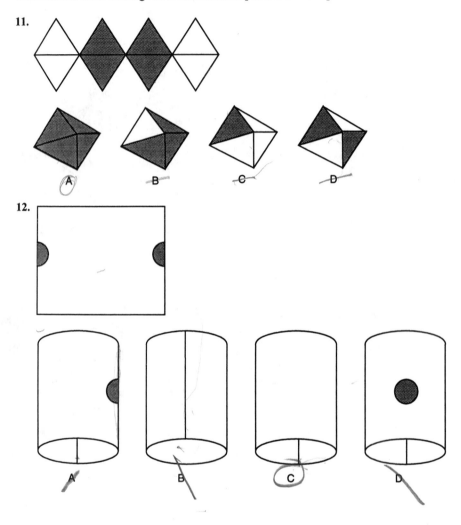

In Exercises 13 and 14, select the drawing (A, B, C, or D) that shows the object in the center being rotated in exactly the same manner as the object being rotated on the first line.

13.

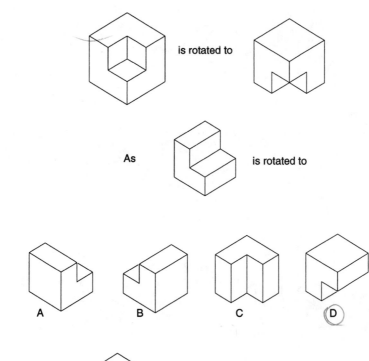

14.

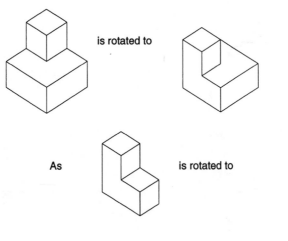

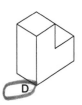

A   B   C   D

In Exercise 15, select the drawing (A, B, C, or D) that shows the object in the center being rotated in exactly the same manner as the object being rotated on the first line.

15.

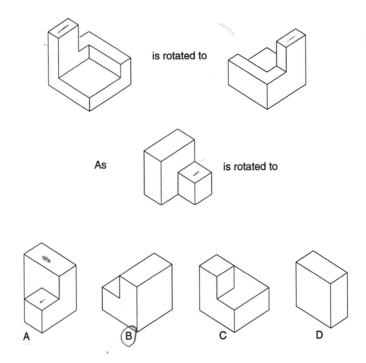

A   B   C   D

REFERENCES

BATTISTA M. T., H. W. GRAYSON, AND G. TALSMA. The Importance of Spatial Visualization and Cognitive Development for Geometry Learning in Preservice Elementary School Teachers. *Journal for Research in Mathematics Education* 13 (1982): 332–340.

BENNETT, G. K., H. G. SEASHORE, AND A. G. WESMAN. *Differential Aptitude Tests, Forms S and T.* New York: The Psychological Corporation, 1973.

BISHOP, J. E. Developing Students' Spatial Ability. *Science Teacher* 45 (1978): 20–23.

BRINKMAN, E. H. Programmed Instruction as a Technique for Improving Spatial Visualization. *Journal of Applied Psychology* 50 (1966): 172–184.

GIMMESTAD, B. J. Gender Differences in Spatial Visualization and Predictors of Success in an Engineering Design Course. *Proceedings of the National Conference on Women in Mathematics and the Sciences.* Sandra Z. and Philip Keith, eds. (St. Cloud, MN: St. Cloud State University, Sept. 1990.) 133–136.

GUAY, R. B. *Purdue Spatial Visualization Test: Rotations.* West Lafayette: Purdue Research Foundation, 1977.

LAPPAN, G. Middle Grades Mathematics Project. Presentation at the National Council of Teachers of Mathematics National Meeting. Detroit, Apr. 1983.

LIKERT, R. *The Revised Minnesota Paper Form Board Test Manual.* New York: The Psychological Corporation, 1970.

OLTMAN, P. K., E. RASKIN, AND H. A. WITKIN. *Group Embedded Figures Test.* Palo Alto: Consulting Psychologists Press, 1971.

2

Developing 3-D Spatial Sense

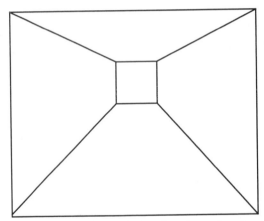

Mind teaser: Is the center of this drawing elevated or depressed?

Answer: It can be viewed either way. It's a paradox.

2.1 *CONSTRUCTION AND ISOMETRIC DRAWINGS OF BUILDINGS*

To develop 3-D spatial sense, one must first construct 3-D objects, observe these objects, and then draw them to scale from different viewpoints. As one's spatial sense develops, it no longer becomes necessary to construct an object before drawing it. A mental image of the object is sufficient to create the drawing. Hence, initially we will work from the concrete object to the more abstract drawing, but ultimately we want to be able to visualize the object and create an accurate drawing of it from this mental image. To become an engineer, one must achieve this level of spatial ability. For example, a mechanical engineer must be able to visualize a machine part and understand how that part will function within a system of parts. The engineer must then be able to communicate the concept for this part with a drawing so that it can be manufactured.

Cubes will be used in the following examples to construct model buildings. The plan for each building will be given by drawing the shape of the top (or base) of the building on square grid paper. Each square will be coded with a number to represent how high the stack of cubes on that square should be. For example, Figure 2.1.1 shows a coded plan and the corresponding building constructed from cubes as viewed from corner X.

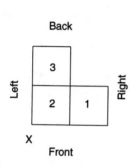

Figure 2.1.1

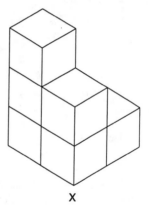

X

A corner view of a building, such as the one shown in Figure 2.1.1, is called an **isometric** view of the building. Such views are easy to draw on isometric dot paper. Isometric dot paper has dots spaced an equal distance apart in a triangular pattern. An important feature of isometric dot paper should be mentioned. When rotated 90°, isometric dot paper does not have the same properties for drawing that it did with its original orientation. Figure 2.1.2 shows Figure 2.1.1 drawn on isometric dot paper. Note that Figure 2.1.2 has fewer lines than Figure 2.1.1. When drawing a building, it is not necessary to outline each cube; rather a line is drawn only where there is an edge to the building. An **edge** can be defined as a line that results from the intersection of two plane surfaces. Isometric drawings are useful for showing a 3-D representation of a building on a flat (2-D) piece of paper.

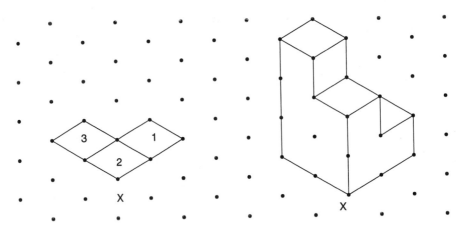

Figure 2.1.2

Sometimes it is easier to think of an object as a collection of surfaces. The isometric drawing of the object can then be made by sketching each visible surface. This process is demonstrated in Figure 2.1.3. In this figure, each surface on the object is drawn individually until all visible surfaces are drawn.

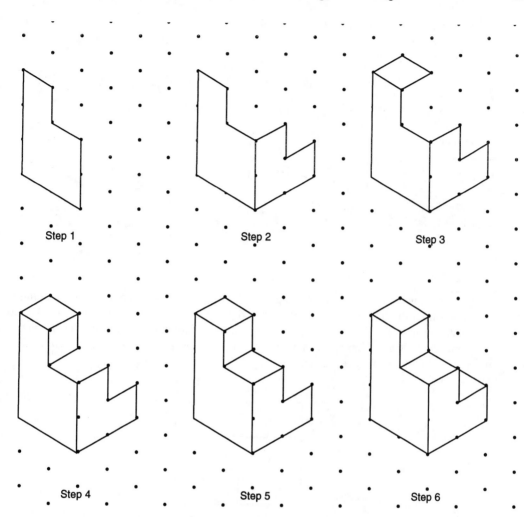

Step 1   Step 2   Step 3

Step 4   Step 5   Step 6

Figure 2.1.3

Figure 2.1.4 shows another coded plan, the corresponding building constructed from cubes, and the final isometric drawing of the building. This time the building is being viewed from corner Y.

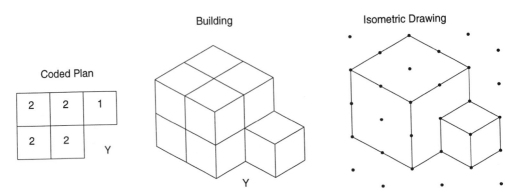

Figure 2.1.4

One way to visualize corner views without disturbing the cubes in your building is to construct the building on 2 cm×2 cm grid paper (sometimes called a *mat*) and then to rotate the mat. Figure 2.1.5 shows the coded plan of a building on a mat being viewed from corner X and from corner Y by rotation of the mat. The mat could also be rotated so that the building could be viewed from corner W or from corner Z.

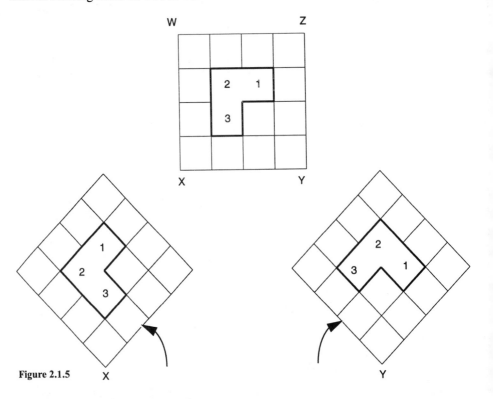

Figure 2.1.5

Isometric grid paper is a popular tool in engineering for drawing isometric views of buildings. One can construct isometric grid paper from isometric dot paper by connecting the dots that lie in the same diagonal lines and in the same vertical lines. Figure 2.1.6 shows isometric grid paper being constructed from isometric dot paper. There is really no

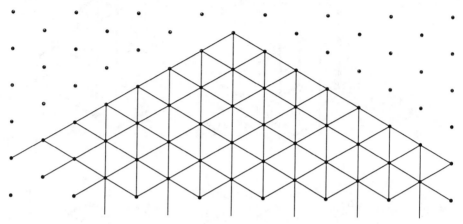

Figure 2.1.6

need to construct your own isometric grid paper—it is commercially available. The motivation for showing the relationship between the two types of paper is to make it easier for a student who can draw buildings on isometric dot paper to transfer those skills to isometric grid paper. Isometric views of buildings can be drawn either directly on isometric grid paper by using a dark marker or on a piece of tracing paper or Vellum placed over the isometric grid paper.

Figure 2.1.7 shows the four corner views of a building on isometric grid paper. The coded plan for the building can be completely determined by viewing the building from its corners, as shown in Figure 2.1.8.

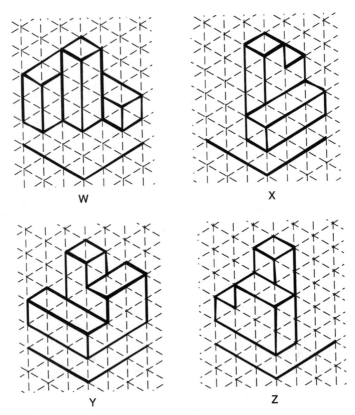

W   X

Y   Z

Figure 2.1.7

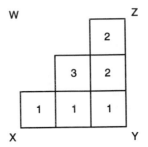

Figure 2.1.8

EXERCISES 2.1

In Exercises 1 and 2, sketch the coded plan for the building shown. Assume that there are no hidden cubes.

1.

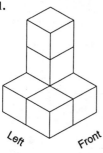

2.

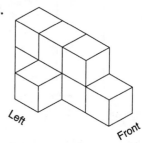

In Exercises 3 to 8, construct the building shown in the coded plan using cubes on a mat. Then rotate the mat to view the building from the identified corner, and sketch the corner view of the building on isometric dot paper. Lines should be drawn only for visible edges of the buildings.

3.

3	3
2	1

X

4.

2	2	2
1	1	1

Y

5.

2	2	
1	1	1
	1	

Y

6.

3	3	
1	1	2
	1	

X

7.

	2	3
1	1	1
	1	

X

8.

	2
2	1
3	1

Y

In Exercises 9 and 10, construct the building shown in the coded plan using cubes on the mat. Then rotate the mat and view the building from corners W, X, Y, and Z. Draw each corner view on isometric grid paper.

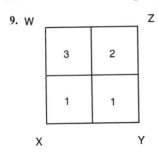

In Exercises 11 to 14, a coded plan and an indicated corner are given for each building. Without actually constructing the building, try to imagine what it looks like. Now draw the building from that corner on isometric dot paper.

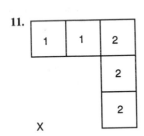

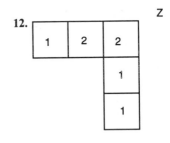

15. On isometric dot paper, draw two different views of a unit cube (i.e., a cube with $1 \times 1 \times 1$ dimensions). In the first view of the cube, the top should be visible. In the second view of the cube, the bottom should be visible.

16. A **wedge** is defined as a $2 \times 1 \times 1$ block cut in half diagonally. On isometric dot paper, draw at least two different views of a wedge.

2.2 ORTHOGRAPHIC DRAWINGS

Isometric sketches are useful for showing a 3-D representation of a solid object on a flat (2-D) piece of paper. However, there are many instances where isometric sketches do not adequately display information in an understandable form. As an example of this, consider a house. An isometric view of the house would show *qualitatively* what the house looked like from the outside. If, however, one wanted to show the interior of the house and the layout of the rooms on each floor, an isometric view would be particularly confusing because the walls from the rooms would run into each other and overlap. Thus, in order to display the layout of the rooms, an orthographic or plan view is normally used. A **plan view** is drawn as if one is located at some point in space above the floor looking down on it. In this way, one is able to accurately view the sizes and relative locations of all the rooms on a particular floor of a building.

This illustrates an important feature in creating views of a building or an object. In general, the object remains fixed in space, and one "moves" around the object in order to "see" what it looks like from different angular perspectives. An isometric view is created as if one is looking straight down a diagonal of a given cube. By looking down the diagonal, one sees all three dimensions (height, width, and depth) of the object. In a plan view of a house, the observer is located at a point above the floor—the house remains stationary. In this way, only the width and the depth of the floor plan are visible; the height is not.

In general, views that show only two dimensions of an object are called **orthographic** views. Typically, the *top* view (sometimes referred to as *plan view*) is one where the object's width and depth are displayed; the *front* view shows the width and the height of an object; and the *side* view of an object shows its depth and height. Figure 2.2.1 illustrates the relationship between dimensions and orthographic view (consider depth as the dimension perpendicular to the plane of the paper.). Note that any two views will display all of the necessary information associated with a given object, but a third view is usually added for clarity.

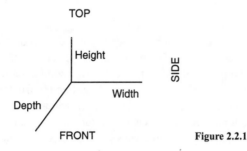

Figure 2.2.1

Figure 2.2.2 shows how orthographic views are created from the geometry of a 3-D object. In creating orthographic views, one imagines that the object is surrounded by a

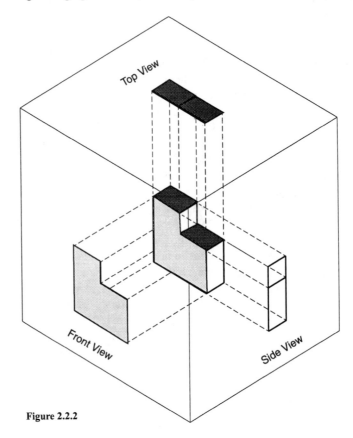

Figure 2.2.2

glass cube. Each of the orthographic views is created by projecting an edge of the object onto one of the panes of glass. The edges are projected so that the "projection rays" are perpendicular to the panes of glass (the term *orthographic* comes from the Greek *ortho*, meaning perpendicular). These projection rays outline the front and side views on vertical panes of the glass cube and the top view on a horizontal pane. Once the object has been projected onto the three panes of glass in the surrounding cube, it is common practice to "unfold" the cube to display the three views of the object in a standard layout. Figure 2.2.3 shows this practice.

In the system of orthographic projection, there are six principal views labeled front, top, back, bottom, and right and left side views. Once the transparent cube is unfolded, the orthographic views of the object are shown in a standard drawing layout. This layout

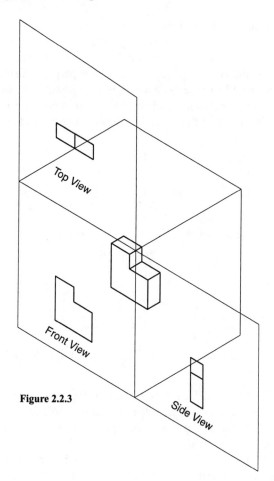

Figure 2.2.3

typically consists of the top, front, and right side views of the object. Figure 2.2.4 shows the standard drawing layout for the three orthographic views of the object in Figure 2.2.3. Note that in this system of orthographic projection, the edges from one view project perpendicularly into the adjacent views.

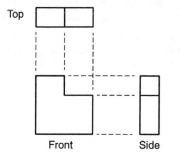

Top

Front   Side   **Figure 2.2.4**

When objects are built out of blocks, all surfaces on the building are normal surfaces. **Normal surfaces** are defined as those parallel to either the front, side, or top orthographic views. Note that a surface parallel to the front view is perpendicular to both the top and the side views; a surface parallel to the top view is perpendicular to the front and side views; and a surface parallel to the side view is perpendicular to the front and top views. A normal surface parallel to the front view is seen in the front view in true size and shape, and is seen as an edge (line) in both the top and side views. Figure 2.2.5 illustrates this principle.

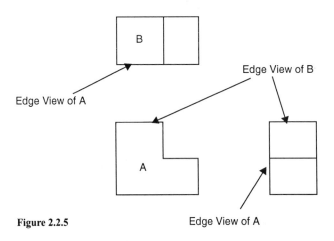

Figure 2.2.5   Edge View of A

In this figure, surface A is parallel to the front view and is seen there in its true shape and size. It is seen as an edge in both the top and the side views, as labeled in the figure. Similarly, surface B is seen true size in the top view and is seen as an edge in both the front and the side views.

One of the advantages of using orthographic views to describe an object is that the object appears undistorted, i.e., the planes appear true size and true shape, and the angles appear true size. Thus, one is able to measure the relative sizes of angles and lengths. This is not the case in isometric drawings. As an example, consider the case of a cube. In reality, we know that all of the faces of the cube meet at right angles. However, when an isometric view of a cube is constructed, if one was to use a protractor to measure the angle between the faces, the angle would be either 60° or 120°; whereas, in orthographic views, the angles between sides would all measure 90°. The reason for this is that with orthographic projection, the faces of the cube are parallel to the viewing plane. In isometric drawings, however, none of the faces of the cube is parallel to the viewing plane. Figure 2.2.6 graphically shows the difference between measured angles in isometric and orthographic viewing.

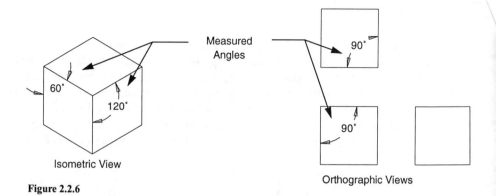

Measured Angles

Isometric View

Orthographic Views

Figure 2.2.6

As in writing, where rules of grammar are needed for effective written communication, rules for making orthographic drawings are needed for effective graphical communication. One of the rules to be followed is that the orthographic views of an object should be aligned with one another. Figure 2.2.7 illustrates this principle.

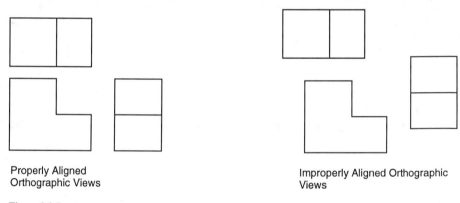

Properly Aligned
Orthographic Views

Improperly Aligned Orthographic
Views

Figure 2.2.7

When creating an orthographic drawing or sketch, lines are drawn at the edges of the object. Sometimes when constructing an engineering drawing, there are edges of an object that are hidden from a particular viewing angle. These hidden edges are drawn as dashed lines and are referred to as **hidden lines**; whereas the visible edges are drawn as solid lines. Solid lines are also referred to as **object lines**. In standard drawing practice, if an object line coincides with a hidden line, then only the object line is shown.

Two orthographic views of an object are adequate to communicate what a 3-D object looks like because each orthographic view gives a different pair of dimensions. For example, a top view will show the length and depth, and a front view will show the length and height, so all three dimensions are represented and the object is completely defined. When an object has an unusual feature, such as an inclined surface (see Section 2.3), it will be accurately defined by two orthographic views if and only if those two views are carefully chosen—not just any two views will do. In Figure 2.2.8, five orthographic views of a building are drawn on square dot paper. Note the use of hidden lines and the use of object lines in this drawing. An isometric view of the building is shown in Figure 2.2.9.

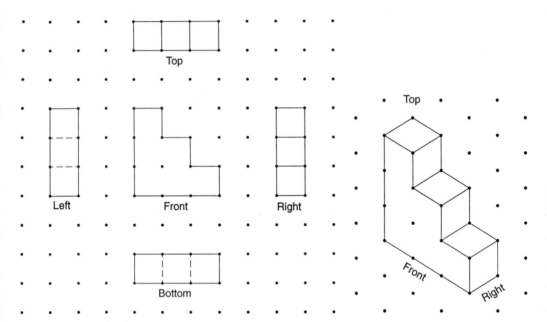

Figure 2.2.8   **Figure 2.2.9**

Many times only two orthographic views of an object are given, and one is expected to draw the third view. This process is easier if one visualizes the way each of the surfaces of the object appears in the third view. For example, suppose the two views of the object shown in Figure 2.2.10 were given and the third (right side) view was required.

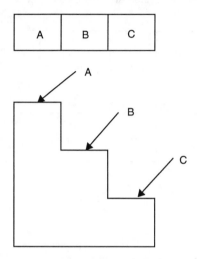

Figure 2.2.10

The surfaces visible in the top view have been labeled A, B, and C. These surfaces are seen as edges in the front and side views because they are normal surfaces. To draw these surfaces in the side view, project them directly into that view from the front view.

The size of these surfaces in the side view can be obtained from the depth dimension shown in the top view. This is illustrated in Figure 2.2.11.To complete the right side view of the object, fill in the front, back, and bottom surfaces. In this example, the back surface is identical to the front surface, otherwise hidden lines would be visible in the front view. Figure 2.2.12 shows the completed drawing of the object.

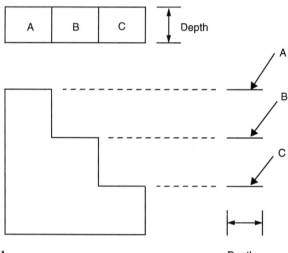

Figure 2.2.11   Depth

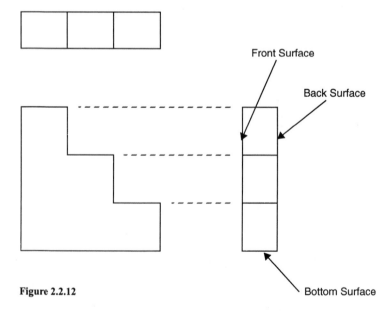

Figure 2.2.12   Bottom Surface

On other occasions, one is given the three orthographic views of an object and is required to create an isometric drawing of it. This can be accomplished by using the *box method*. When creating an isometric drawing by this method, first sketch a box on isometric grid paper. The dimensions of this box are the overall dimensions of the object as seen in the orthographic views. This step is shown in Figure 2.2.13.

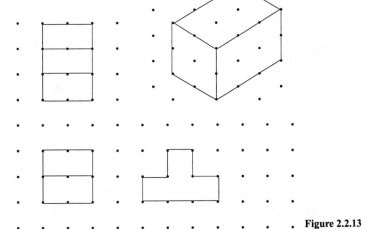

Figure 2.2.13

After sketching the defining box, draw each of the orthographic views of the object on the corresponding faces of the box, as illustrated in Figure 2.2.14. Remove and add lines from this box until all of the features in the orthographic views are shown. This results in the final isometric view of the object shown in Figure 2.2.15.

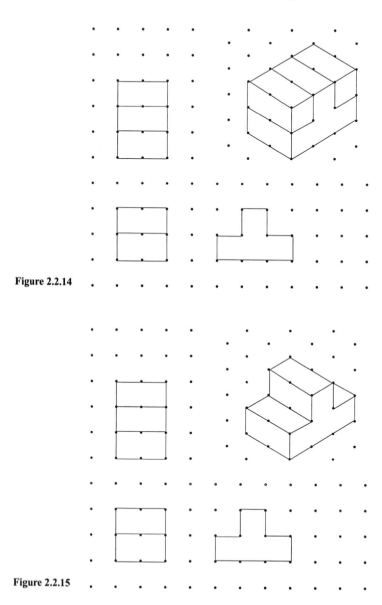

Figure 2.2.14

Figure 2.2.15

EXERCISES 2.2

In Exercises 1 to 4, construct the building shown with cubes on a mat. Assume there are no hidden cubes. Rotate the mat to observe the front and right-side views. Face the front of the building and look down at it to observe the top view. On square dot paper, sketch the three standard orthographic views in a standard drawing layout.

1.   **2.**

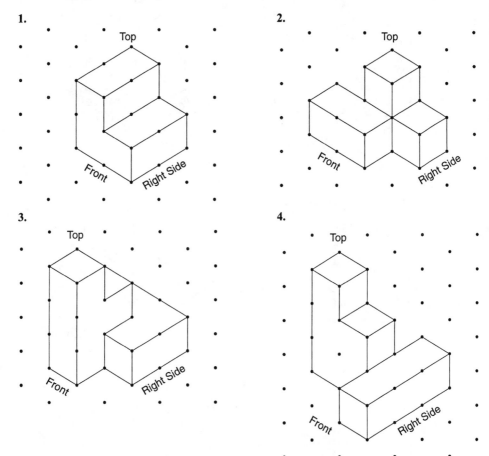

3.   **4.**

In Exercises 5 to 8, an isometric view of a building is given. Assume there are no hidden cubes. Without constructing the building, try to visualize the top view, the front view, and the right view. Sketch all three of these views on square dot paper in a standard drawing layout.

5.

6.

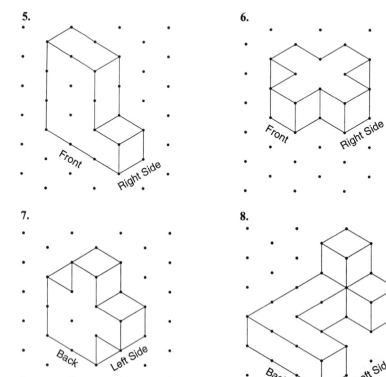

7.

8.

In Exercises 9 to 12, use isometric dot paper to construct the isometric view of the object shown in orthographic projection. The isometric view should show both the front and the right side of the object.

9.

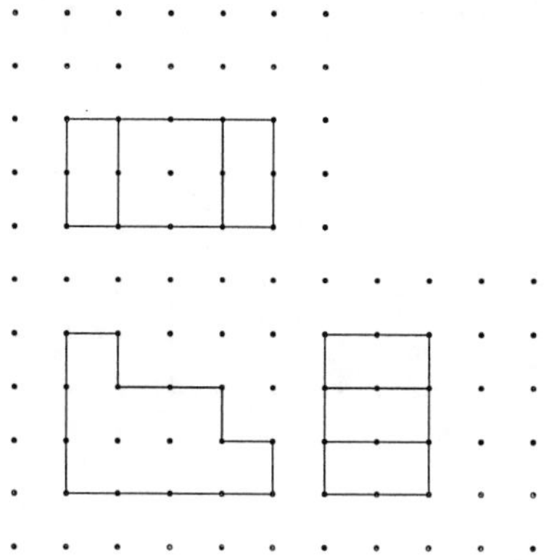

10.

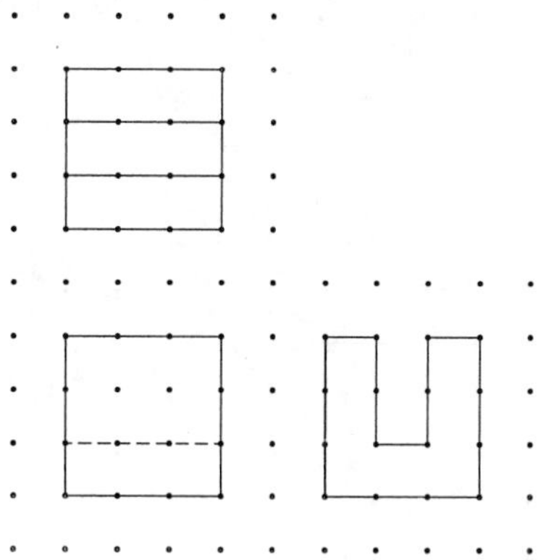

11.

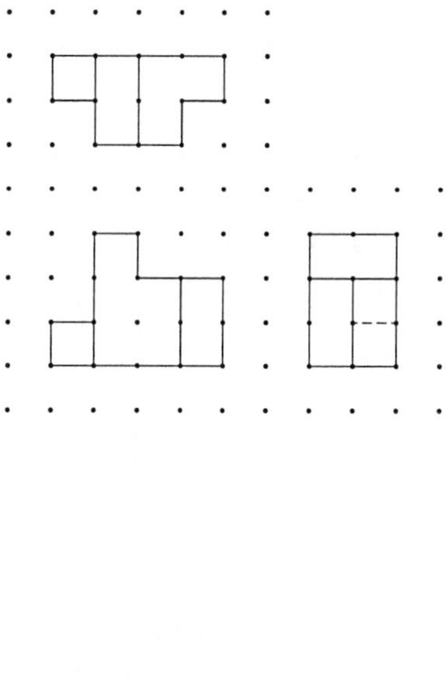

12.

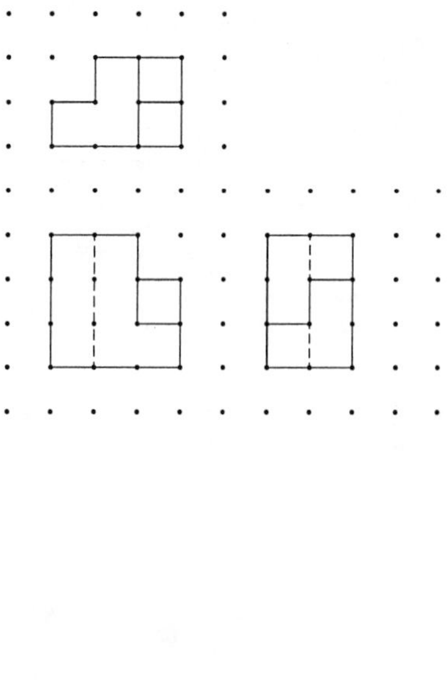

In Exercises 13 to 16, sketch the two orthographic views on a separate sheet and then construct the missing orthographic view.

13.

14.

15.

16.

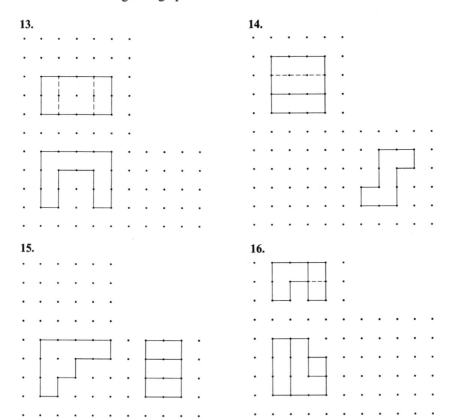

2.3 *INCLINED SURFACES*

So far in our discussion of isometric and orthographic drawings, we have limited our consideration to normal surfaces only. Although normal surfaces alone can be used to demonstrate the principles of constructing orthographic and isometric views of an object, their primary disadvantage is that very few "real life" objects are made up entirely of normal surfaces. In contrast with normal surfaces, **inclined surfaces** are defined as those surfaces that meet two of the orthographic views at an angle and are perpendicular to the third orthographic view. Thus, inclined surfaces appear as a surface in two of the orthographic views and as an edge (line) in the third view. Because inclined surfaces are not parallel to any of the orthographic views, they do not appear as true size in any of the orthographic views. Figure 2.3.1 illustrates an inclined surface in an object and the corresponding projected views.

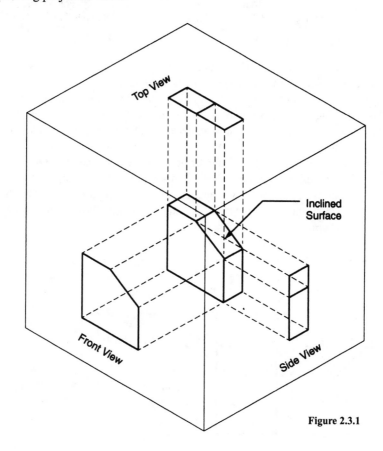

Figure 2.3.1

Figure 2.3.2 shows the orthographic views for the object in Figure 2.3.1 and the orthographic views for the object in Figure 2.2.2. As can be seen from this figure, the top and side views for the two objects are identical, and the general shapes of the objects are

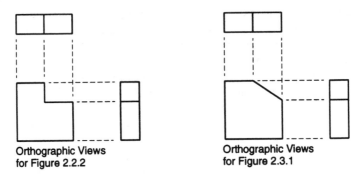

Orthographic Views
for Figure 2.2.2

Orthographic Views
for Figure 2.3.1

Figure 2.3.2

shown in the corresponding front views. Note that the front views are absolutely necessary for the complete description of the objects: without them, one would not be able to tell exactly what the objects look like. Note also that the size of the inclined surface in the right-side view is different from its apparent size in the top view. Neither of these views shows the surface in true size, because the surface is not parallel to either view. The size of the surface in both views is smaller than the actual size of the surface. When inclined surfaces are projected into orthographic views, they become *foreshortened.*

To construct an inclined surface in an isometric drawing, one typically locates the two endpoints of each inclined edge and draws a straight line between them. Figure 2.3.3 illustrates how inclined edges are located in isometric views, and Figure 2.3.4 shows the resulting isometric drawing of the object.

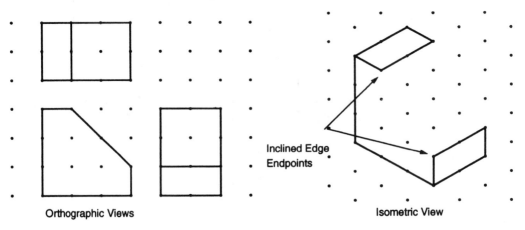

Inclined Edge
Endpoints

Orthographic Views

Isometric View

Figure 2.3.3

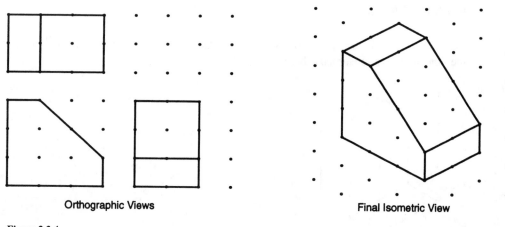

Orthographic Views   Final Isometric View

Figure 2.3.4

When constructing isometric views of objects that contain inclined surfaces, one should be careful to select an orientation of the object that makes the inclined surface appear as a surface and not as an edge. Figure 2.3.5 shows the two possible orientations of the object shown in Figure 2.3.4. As can be seen from Figure 2.3.5, the view labeled Isometric 1 shows the inclined surface as a surface, whereas the view labeled Isometric 2 shows this surface as an edge. The second view does not present a clear representation of the appearance of the object. This uncertainty should be avoided to achieve effective graphical communication.

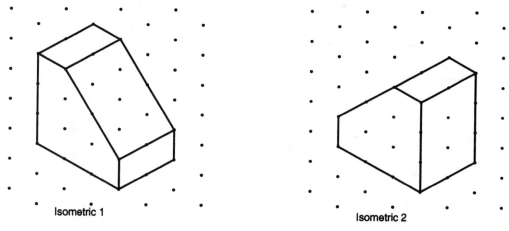

Isometric 1   Isometric 2

Figure 2.3.5

EXERCISES 2.3

In Exercises 1 to 4, use square dot paper to construct the top, front, and right side views of
the objects shown in isometric below.

1.

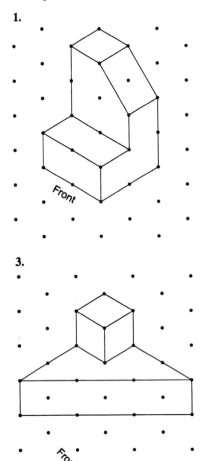

2.

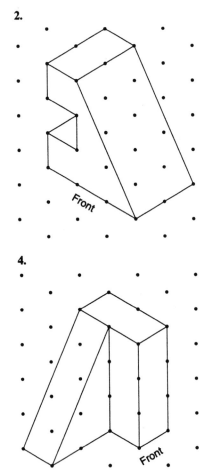

3.

4.

In Exercises 5 to 8, use isometric dot paper to construct an isometric view of the objects shown in orthographic projection below. The isometric view should show both the front and the right side of the object.

5.

6.

7.

8.

2.4 SINGLE-CURVED SURFACES

Many objects contain surfaces that are curved in space, and it is important to be able to graphically communicate curved surfaces in an orthographic projection system. **Single-curved surfaces** are defined as those with curvature about one axis only. Typically, this kind of surface is found on a cylindrically shaped object such as an aluminum can. A double-curved surface is spherical in shape, like a basketball. In this text, we will limit our discussion of curved surfaces to single-curved surfaces only.

When single-curved surfaces are drawn, only the outer limits of the curved surface are projected into orthographic views. The curvature of the surface will be visible in an adjacent view. Thus, a cylinder will project as a circle in one orthographic view and as a rectangle in the other two orthographic views. This is illustrated in Figure 2.4.1.

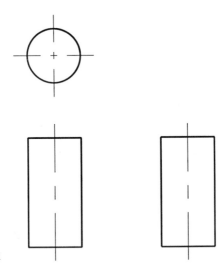

Figure 2.4.1

Because single-curved surfaces do not show their curvature in all of the orthographic views, it is customary to use **centerlines** to designate the location of the center of curvature for the surfaces. Centerlines are shown as a long dash followed by a short dash followed by a long dash, as illustrated in Figure 2.4.1. In this case, two centerlines are included in the view of the cylinder that shows the circular end (top view) and one centerline is shown in each of the views where the curved surface appears as a rectangle (front and side views).

Most of the time, single-curved surfaces will appear as interior, cylindrical holes in objects. The principle involved in drawing these interior surfaces is the same as in drawing exterior surfaces, except that they now appear as hidden features on the drawing. Figure 2.4.2 shows a three-view drawing of a block with two holes in it. One hole extends all the way through the object, but the other hole does not.

Single-curved surfaces will appear as ellipses in isometric views. An ellipse can usually be sketched as four circular arcs which are tangent to each other. To sketch a cylinder using isometric dot or grid paper, begin by drawing the visible or upper ellipse.

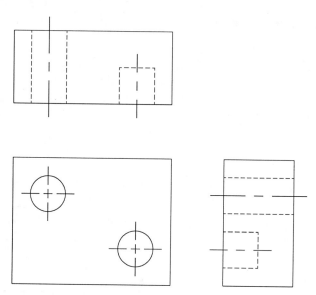

Figure 2.4.2

Locate the four points that correspond to the radial limits of the circular surface. This is shown in stage 1 of Figure 2.4.3. Then sketch in the two longer elliptical arcs as shown in stage 2 of Figure 2.4.3. Finish by sketching in the remaining two arcs to form the complete ellipse. The remaining arcs will be tangent to the first arcs and will go through the other two radial points. This is shown in stage 3 of Figure 2.4.3. To finish the isometric sketch of the cylinder, show the outer limits of the curved surface with straight lines "perpendicular" to the circular surface. Once the straight edges are drawn, sketch in a half ellipse at the bottom of the cylinder, as shown in stage 4 of Figure 2.4.3. Sketching ellipses in isometric views may require some practice before you can achieve acceptable results.

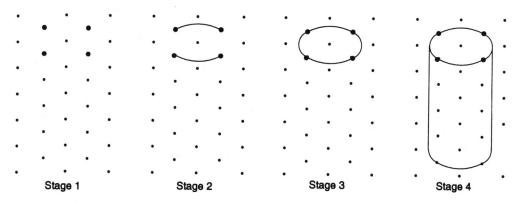

Stage 1   Stage 2   Stage 3   Stage 4

Figure 2.4.3

EXERCISES 2.4

In Exercises 1 to 3, for the objects shown in isometric view, sketch the top, front, and right side views. Be sure to include centerlines in your sketches.

1.   **2.**

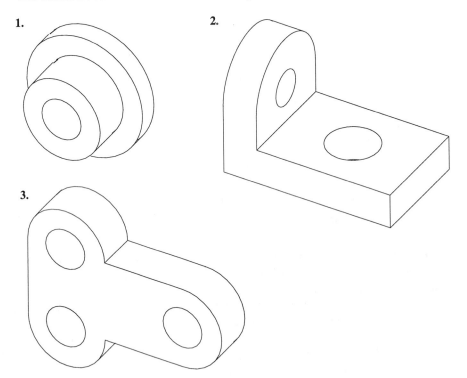

3.

In Exercises 4 to 7, using isometric dot paper, sketch the isometric views of the objects shown in orthographic projection below.

4.   **5.**

6.   **7.**

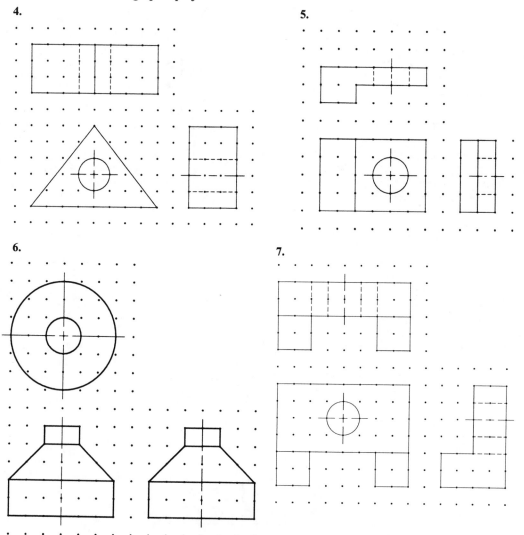

For Exercises 8 to 10, using square dot paper, sketch the missing view for the objects shown.

8.

9.

10.

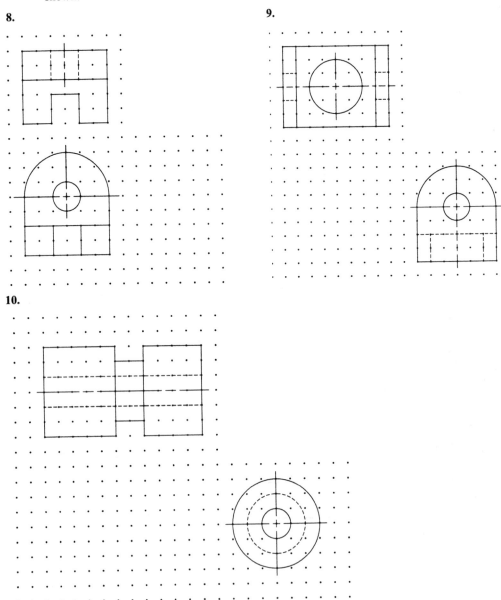

2.5 OBLIQUE SURFACES

Oblique surfaces are neither parallel nor perpendicular to any of the principal orthographic views. Therefore, they appear as similarly shaped surfaces in each of the top, front, and right side views. Figure 2.5.1 shows the orthographic projection for an oblique surface. In this case, the oblique surface is formed by "cutting off" one corner of a block.

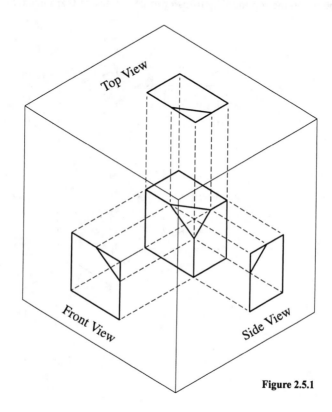

Figure 2.5.1

Oblique surfaces are more difficult to visualize than other types of surfaces because they are seen neither as edges nor as true size in any of the orthographic views. To create the third view of an oblique surface, it is easiest to determine the location of the points defining the surface and then to "connect the dots." The same procedure can be followed for creating an isometric view of an oblique surface. Figure 2.5.2 shows the procedure for creating the third view and an isometric view of an oblique surface. The points are numbered on the top to make it easier to keep track of them in each view.

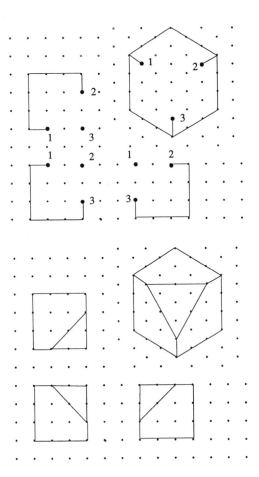

Figure 2.5.2

Figure 2.5.3 shows three orthographic views and an isometric view of a more complicated object that contains an oblique surface. Look at the views of the object, and verify the location of the points on the oblique surface in each view.

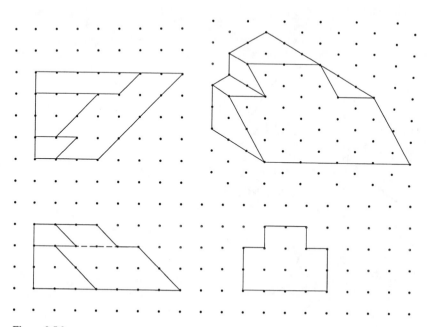

Figure 2.5.3

EXERCISES 2.5

For Exercises 1 to 3, sketch the top, front, and right side views from the isometric view shown below.

1.

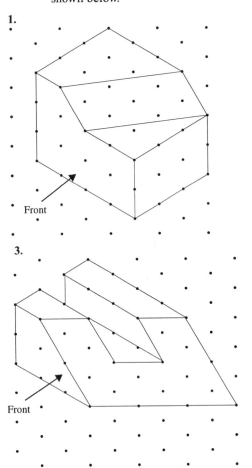

2.

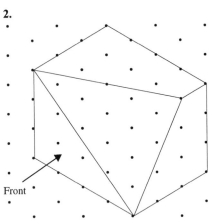

Front

3.

Front

For Exercises 4 to 7, using square dot paper, sketch the missing view for the objects shown.

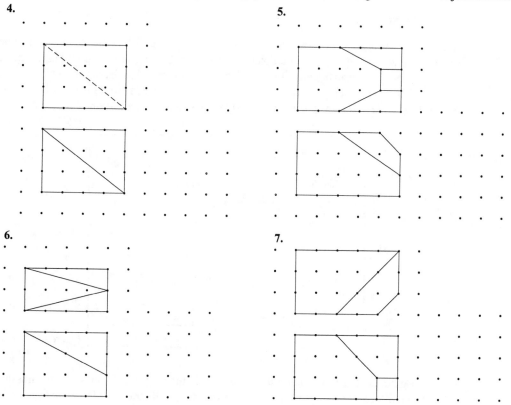

4.

5.

6.

7.

2.6 APPLICATIONS

Engineering

Complete engineering drawings typically have at least three orthographic views and one isometric view. The layout for a complete engineering drawing is shown in Figure 2.6.1. These drawings enable an engineer to see an object's distinguishing features quickly. Recall, however, that two orthographic views are all that are really needed to define an object. The extra orthographic and isometric views are added to ease the visualization of the object.

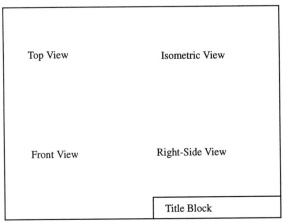

Figure 2.6.1

In Figure 2.6.2, the top and front view of a building are given. What would the missing right side view look like? What would the corresponding isometric view look like?

Answers to these questions can be found in Figure 2.6.3, which shows an engineering drawing of the building.

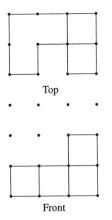

Figure 2.6.2

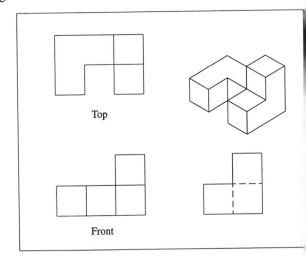

Engineering drawings are made of all types of objects. Figures 2.6.4 and 2.6.5 show engineering drawings for two familiar objects, a coffee mug and a car, respectively. Engineering drawings also typically contain dimensions, notes and labels. These are beyond the scope of this text and will not be shown on engineering drawings here.

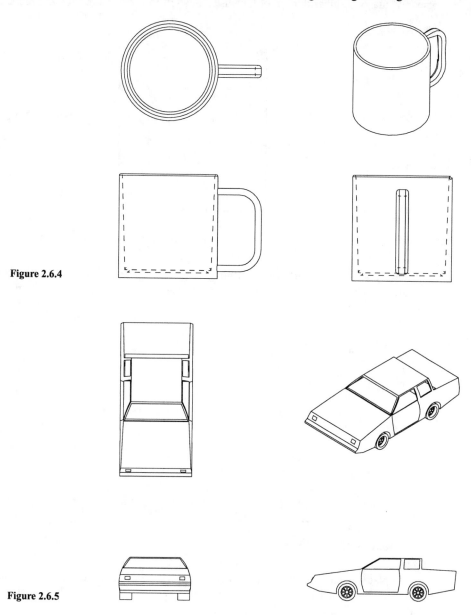

Figure 2.6.4

Figure 2.6.5

Archeology

An archeologist was exploring a remote area in Scotland. Excavation of the area revealed an ancient castle. The castle had been constructed using large cubes of stone cut from a nearby quarry. A clear outline of the castle was left in the ground. Figure 2.6.6 shows the

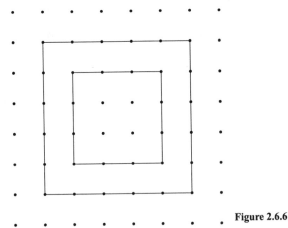

Figure 2.6.6

outline of the base of the castle. Among the items unearthed were several plates with pictures of what appeared to be views of the castle. Figure 2.6.7 shows two of the pictures

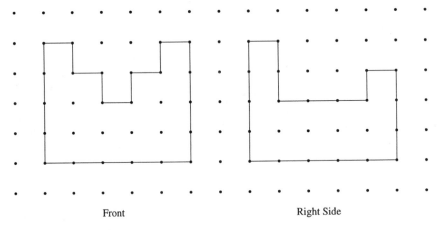

Front   Right Side

Figure 2.6.7

on the plates, which the archeologist believed were the front and right views of the castle. Based on Figures 2.6.6 and 2.6.7, a friendly civil engineer drew the archeologist a plausible 3-D sketch of the castle (see Figure 2.6.8).

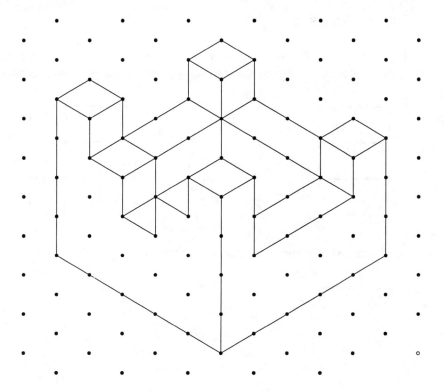

Figure 2.6.8

EXERCISES 2.6

For Exercises 1 and 2, sketch the engineering drawing layout for the building shown in each coded plan. Use the engineering drawing layout paper provided in Appendix II.

1.

3	3
1	1
1	1

2.

2	3	2
1	2	2
1		1

3. The figure below shows an isometric view of a wing nut. Sketch its front view.

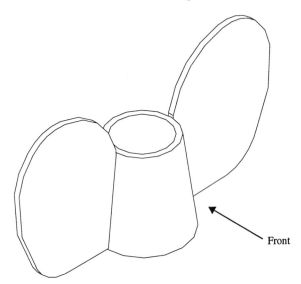

Front

4. Sketch an engineering drawing layout of a table.

5. Sketch an engineering drawing layout of a stapler.

6. Sketch an engineering drawing layout of a telephone.

7. The Berlin Wall divided the German city of Berlin for 28 years. At the stroke of midnight, November 9, 1989, the wall began to tumble down. Berliners used ropes and chains to pull down huge sections of the wall. A news photographer recorded the following views of a damaged section of the wall; draw an isometric view of it.

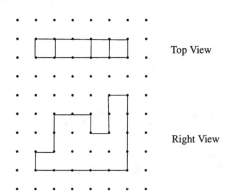

Top View

Right View

8. The Great Wall of China was constructed many centuries ago using large blocks of stone. The wall is wide enough that people can walk and even pull carts on it. Thus, the wall is much like a road along the ancient Chinese border. Along both sides of the wall are raised sections for protection, and gaps are located at regular intervals along these sections. The total height of a raised section is eight blocks, and the width of a section is two blocks. The gaps are located such that there are six blocks of stone and then a gap two blocks wide. This pattern repeats throughout the length of the wall. Shown below are two orthographic views of a raised section of the wall. Using isometric dot paper, construct an isometric sketch of the section.

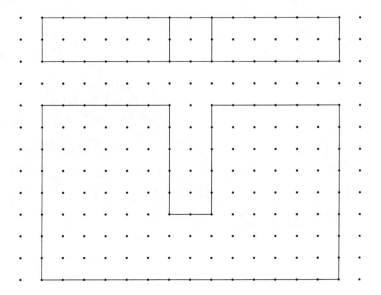

3

Flat Pattern Development of Solids

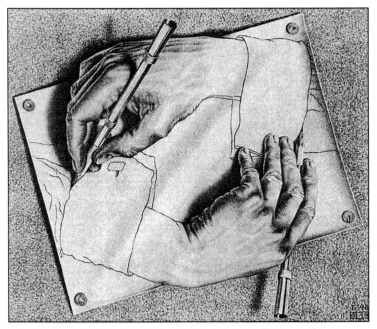

Mind teaser*: What gives the hands in this picture the appearance of being 3-dimensional?   *Answer:* The shading.

3.1 2-D PATTERNS FOLDED INTO 3-D OBJECTS

The ability to construct a flat pattern for a 3-D object is a special kind of spatial ability. One way to acquire this ability is to work with paper models, disassemble them, and observe the patterns that created them. Figure 3.1.1 shows a paper cylinder as it is cut apart and unfolded. We say that the cylinder has a flat pattern of two circles and a rectangle. The length of the longer side of the rectangle is equal to the circumference of the circles. Flat patterns of cylinders have widespread use. A tomato soup can, for example, would have such a pattern stamped out of steel.

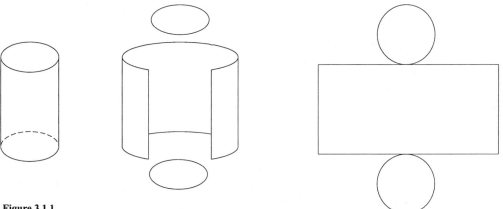

Figure 3.1.1

Sometimes the surfaces of an object are shaded, colored, or marked differently. This somewhat complicates the design of a flat pattern for the object. Careful visualization of how the surfaces will fold together is needed to draw an accurate flat pattern for the object. Imagine a paper cube with the word CUBE spelled out on four of its sides, with one letter per side. Figure 3.1.2 gives an isometric view of such a cube, along with two possible flat patterns it.

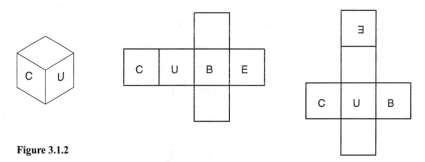

Figure 3.1.2

The solid lines represent **fold lines** where two plane surfaces of the cube will intersect. If you have difficulty imagining that both of these patterns would create such a cube, trace the patterns from Figure 3.1.2 onto a piece of paper, cut them out, and fold them up into cubes. Note that more than one geometric design for a flat pattern solves this problem.

When given a flat pattern, one must be able to visualize and draw the object that would be created if the pattern were cut out, folded, and constructed. It is important to realize that the shading is only on one side of the pattern. In Figure 3.1.3, which house would be constructed from the pattern shown at the left? House A is incorrect because the roof above the door should not be shaded. House B is incorrect because the roof above the circular window should be shaded. House D is incorrect because the side of the house with the door should not be adjacent to the side of the house with the window. The correct answer is House C.

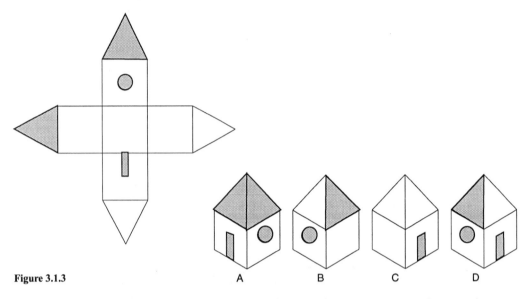

Figure 3.1.3   A   B   C   D

In the actual construction of physical models from flat patterns, it is useful to include tabs on the patterns. **Tabs** are extra pieces that do not contribute to the physical shape of the object but that fold inside the object and give it greater strength. Figure 3.1.4 shows a flat pattern with shaded tabs for a cube. In the case of paper models, tabs provide a surface for gluing the folded pattern together. Tabs are easy to add to any flat pattern and are not a serious spatial visualization task, so most of the flat patterns in this text will not show tabs.

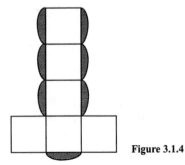

Figure 3.1.4

EXERCISES 3.1

1. A $3 \times 2 \times 1$ rectangular prism (or block) is shown below. Draw a 2-D pattern on square grid paper for construction of the prism.

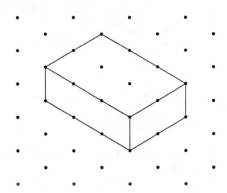

2. The picture below shows an oblong solid. Draw a 2-D pattern on square grid paper for the solid.

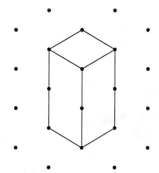

3. Sketch the 3-D solid that would result from cutting out and folding up the pattern shown below.

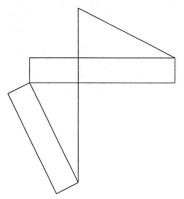

4. Sketch the 3-D solid that would result from cutting out and folding up the pattern shown below.

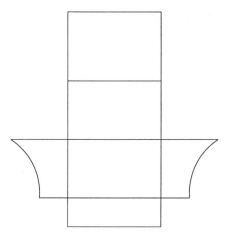

5. Which house could be constructed from the pattern at the left?

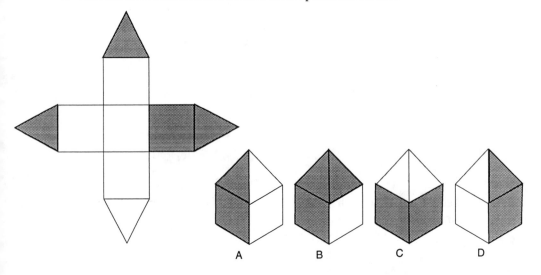

6. Which mining shaft could be constructed from the pattern at the left?

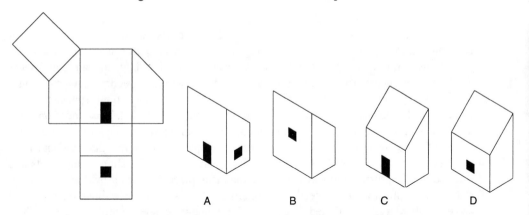

A   B   C   D

7. Which water fountain cup could be constructed from the pattern at the left?

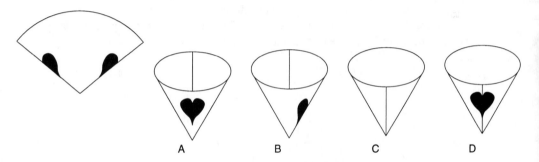

A   B   C   D

8. Which die could be constructed from the pattern at the left?

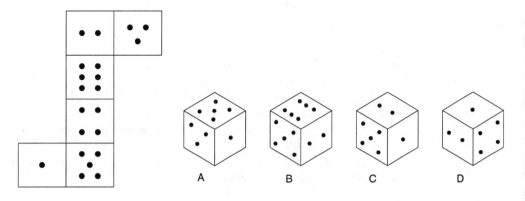

A   B   C   D

3.2 APPLICATIONS

Sheet metal is typically made out of thin (less than ¼") galvanized steel. One of its primary uses in the industrial setting is for use in ducts, which carry heat and air conditioning through buildings. Straight, regular-shaped duct work is available in standard sizes. However, in creating all the duct work necessary in a building, custom-made pieces are sometimes necessary for going around corners, changing directions, or providing a transition from one size of duct work to another. In order to make these specialized 3-D pieces out of a flat sheet of metal, pattern developments are created. These developments are made true size so that they can be placed directly on the sheet metal and cut out. Tabs are usually placed at the seam line of a pattern development so that the final product can be put together easily. When sheet metal is worked, tabs are usually slipped into joints and screwed to other surfaces to add strength to the metal piece. Besides providing the general shape for cutting the sheet metal, the pattern is also used to scribe lines on the metal showing where it is to be folded. The final 3-D product is achieved by folding the cut sheet metal into the desired shape. Once the piece is folded, the seam line is fastened using the tabs. Because duct work is usually open at each end to allow for the free flow of air through a building, typical pattern developments are open-ended.

Figure 3.2.1 shows an isometric view of a 3-D shape that requires a flat pattern development. In order to create the flat pattern development for this open-ended object,

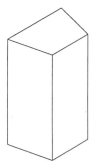

Figure 3.2.1

one should first imagine drawing a line all the way around the perimeter of the object. This line is usually around the bottom of the object and is called the **stretch-out line**. One then draws this stretch-out line to the right of the front view as one continuous line segment. This is illustrated in Figure 3.2.2. For this particular object, the true size of the perimeter can be measured in the top view. The lengths of the segments as seen in that view are true length because they are parallel to the top view.

A vertical edge on the object is chosen as the seam line for the development. Typically, the seam line is chosen as the shortest edge. In this case, all edges are the same length; therefore the choice of a seam line is arbitrary. The addition of the tab sections will not be shown in this example. The fold lines for this development are the corners of the object, and the flat pattern development will also include the locations of the fold lines.

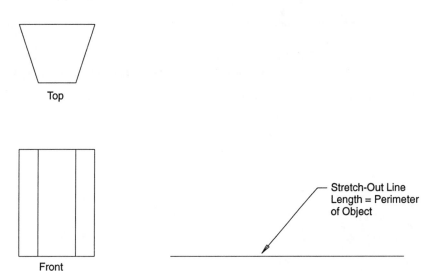

Figure 3.2.2

Note that when viewed from above, the object corners appear as points, and when viewed from the front, the corners appear as straight vertical lines. The next step is to label each object corner in both the front and the top views. Both endpoints of each corner should be labeled. In the top view, the two point labels coincide. This is illustrated in Figure 3.2.3.

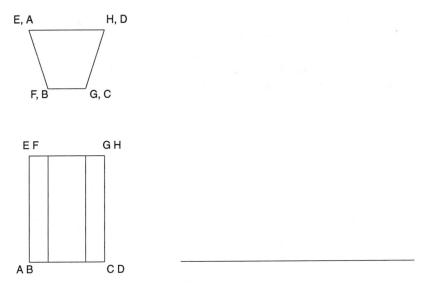

Figure 3.2.3

The bottom corner points (A, B, C, and D) are positioned appropriately along the stretch-out line so that the lengths of these line segments (i.e., AB, BC, CD, and DA) are shown true size. The true lengths of the line segments are obtained in the top view of the object. Figure 3.2.4 shows the placement of these marks on the stretch-out line.

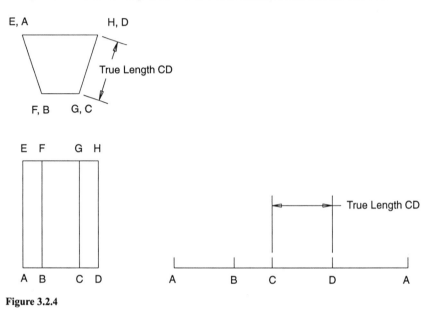

Figure 3.2.4

Note that the development along the stretch-out line begins and ends with the same point. To complete the pattern development, the fold lines (corners) are drawn perpendicular to the stretch-out line. The length of a fold line is equal to the height of the object at each corner. For this object, the true size height is seen in the front view. Figure 3.2.5 shows the completed flat pattern development for the object.

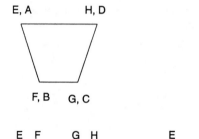

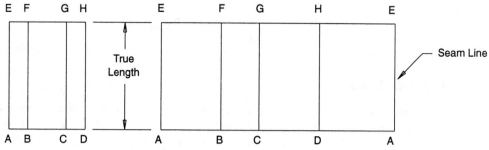

Figure 3.2.5

Figure 3.2.6 shows a flat pattern development for a folded sheet metal part that is not of a uniform height. The procedure used in creating this pattern development is identical

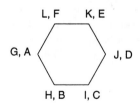

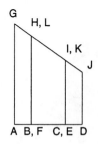

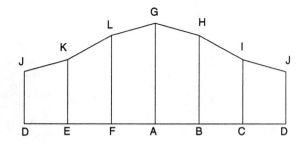

Figure 3.2.6

to the one outlined in the previous example. Note that in this figure, the development starts and ends at point D. This ensures that the shortest fold line is the seam line. Figure 3.2.7 is an isometric view of the object created by folding the pattern shown in Figure 3.2.6.

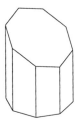

Figure 3.2.7

Platonic Solids

The most ancient polyhedra are the set known as the *five Platonic solids* (named after Plato, the Greek mathematician and philosopher). In general, a **polyhedron** can be defined as a finite region of space enclosed by a finite number of planes. (*Note:* More rigorous definitions of a polyhedron will be given in upper-level geometry and analysis courses.) Each of the Platonic solids encloses space by use of regular polygons. A **regular polygon** is a polygon with sides of equal length and interior angles of equal measure. Thus, the Platonic solids are classified as regular polyhedra. Euclid's book *Elements* (Heath, p.507) concludes with a proof that there are only five regular polyhedra: the *tetrahedron*, the *octahedron*, the *cube*, the *dodecahedron*, and the *icosahedron*.

The simplest of all the Platonic solids is the *tetrahedron*. It has four equilateral triangles for faces. Three triangles meet at each of its four vertices (a **vertex** of a polyhedron is a point where three or more edges meet). Four is the smallest number of triangles possible to enclose a portion of space. A flat pattern with tabs and a 3-D drawing of a tetrahedron are shown in Figure 3.2.8.

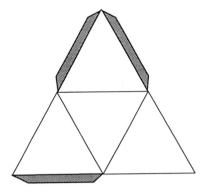

Figure 3.2.8

If one wants to see each face of the tetrahedron in a model, it is helpful to color each triangle differently. To construct the tetrahedron from the pattern, apply glue to the tabs, use the middle triangle as the base, and fold the remaining triangles either up or down.

The *octahedron* is a polyhedron whose faces are eight equilateral triangles. Four triangles meet at each of its six vertices. Figure 3.2.9 shows a pattern and a 3-D drawing of an octahedron. In the figure, only half of the octahedron is visible. The back half is identical to the front half but is oriented in the opposite direction.

Figure 3.2.9

The best known of all the Platonic solids is undoubtedly the *cube,* or, more technically, the *hexahedron.* It has six square faces with three squares meeting at each of its eight vertices. Figure 3.2.10 shows a 3-D drawing of a cube. Two possible patterns for a cube were discussed in Section 3.1. The cube has an interesting property relative to the next Platonic solid. A compound of five cubes can be enclosed by a dodecahedron.

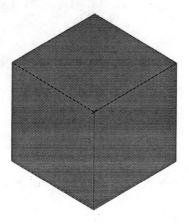

Figure 3.2.10

A *dodecahedron* has twelve regular pentagons for faces. Three pentagons meet at each of its twenty vertices. Figure 3.2.11 shows a pattern and a 3-D drawing of a dodecahedron.

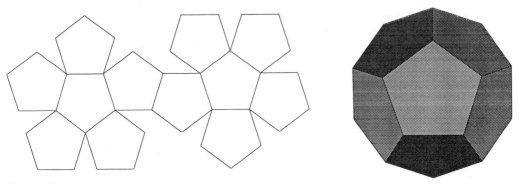

Figure 3.2.11

The last of the Platonic solids is the *icosahedron*. It has twenty equilateral triangles for faces. Five triangles meet at each of its vertices. Figure 3.2.12 shows a pattern and a 3-D drawing of an icosahedron.

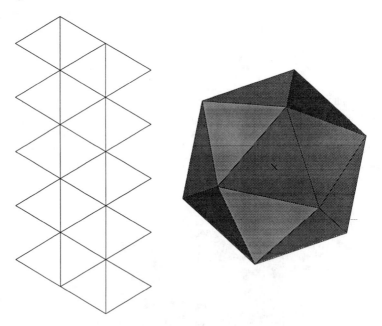

Figure 3.2.12

Other polyhedral solids exist but will not be discussed here. Entire books are devoted to their descriptions and constructions because they allow a variety of polygons as faces and become increasingly complex.

Upholstering and Sewing

Constructing 2-D patterns into 3-D coverings is a basic skill in both upholstering and sewing. In these two professions, pieces of a pattern must be sewn together, so tabs are replaced by seams. These seams are usually about ½" in width.

Consider the upholsterer who wants to make a pattern to re-cover the lamp shade shown in Figure 3.2.13. First, the upholsterer would measure the diameter of each circular base and the slant height. Let d be the diameter of the smaller circular base, D be the

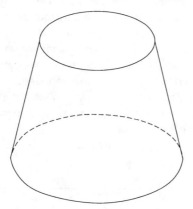

Figure 3.2.13

diameter of the larger circular base, and l be the slant height of the lamp shade. A flat pattern for cutting fabric to re-cover the lamp shade is shown in Figure 3.2.14. A ½" seam will be sewn along the slant height l, and the ½" of fabric along the top and bottom will be folded twice (two ¼" folds) and sewn to make a clean edge.

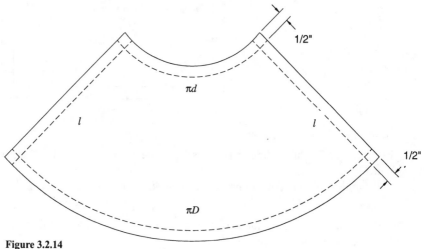

Figure 3.2.14

Concrete Estimation

Engineering is not an exact science. Engineers spend a great deal of time making estimates and approximations during the design process. One of the quantities engineers estimate is the amount of material used in a construction project. An example of material that engineers estimate is the amount of concrete in a basement.

The total amount of concrete necessary consists of the amount in each of the four walls, as well as the amount in the basement floor (or slab). Usually, a basement does not have a concrete ceiling. The amount of concrete in the floor or in a wall is its volume. For each wall or for the floor, the volume is computed by multiplying the surface area by the thickness.

One of the most critical aspects in estimating concrete volumes is keeping track of units. Concrete volumes are usually reported in units of cubic yards. Therefore, dimensions for a basement must be converted to yards either before or after the volume is computed. Recall that there are 3 feet (or 36 inches) in one yard. When reporting volumes of concrete, the word "cubic" is usually left out. Thus, 30 cubic yards of concrete would be reported as 30 yards of concrete (the *cubic* is understood).

Consider the basement floor plan shown in Figure 3.2.15. For this basement floor

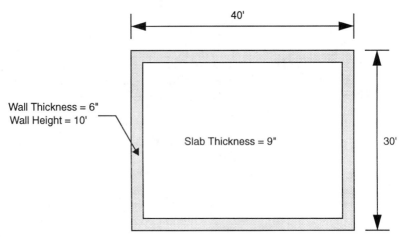

Figure 3.2.15

plan, think about "unfolding" the walls from the floor to obtain the "pattern" shown in Figure 3.2.16.

In this example, the volume of the concrete in the slab is equal to:

$$V_{slab} = A_{slab} \cdot t_{slab}$$

where V = the volume, A = the surface area and t = the thickness. In this case, the volume of concrete in the slab is estimated as

$$V = \qquad\qquad = 33.3 \text{ yd.}$$

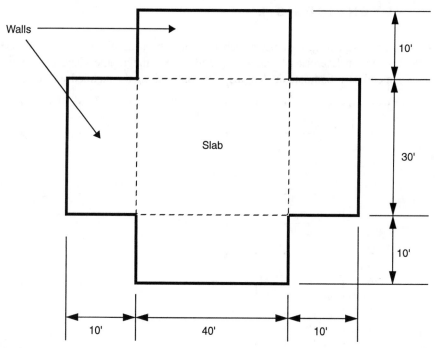

Walls

Slab

10'

30'

10'

10'   40'   10'

Figure 3.2.16

Note the conversion of the given dimensions to yards. Similarly, the total volume in the walls can be computed as follows:

$$V = 2\left(\frac{30}{3} \cdot \frac{10}{3} \cdot \frac{6}{36}\right) + 2\left(\frac{40}{3} \cdot \frac{10}{3} \cdot \frac{6}{36}\right) = 25.9 \text{ yd}$$

Note that in this calculation there are two walls that are 30 feet long and two walls that are 40 feet long. The wall height is 10 feet, and the wall thickness is 6 inches in each case. The total amount of concrete necessary for the construction of this basement is therefore approximately 59.2 yards.

The amount of concrete needed for the project described in the previous example actually would be less than 59.2 yards. The pipes and reinforcing materials in the slab and in the walls will take up some of the volume. Windows in the basement walls will also take up some of the volume. Sometimes, the basement walls will not all have the same height or thickness, so care should be taken when making these calculations. For example, if you are making calculations for a walk-out basement with sliding glass doors along part of one basement wall, the volume of concrete needed will be less.

EXERCISES 3.2

Using square grid paper, sketch the flat pattern developments for the sheet metal parts shown in Exercises 1 and 2. Top and front orthographic views are given for each sheet metal part. Estimate the lengths of the sides along the inclined surfaces.

1.

2.

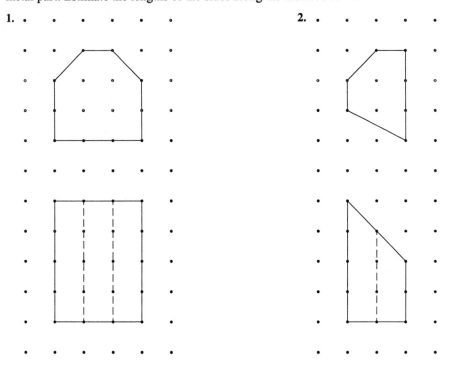

Construction hints: Polyhedral models are sturdier if the patterns are done on construction paper rather than on typing paper. Glue sticks are less messy than bottled glue for gluing the models together. Before folding, trace over solid lines using a ballpoint pen and a ruler. This will ensure accurate folds.

In Exercises 3 to 5, use an equilateral triangle the size of the one shown below to create your patterns. Answers may vary.

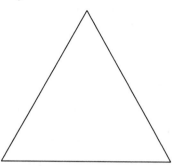

3. Construct a pattern for a tetrahedron like the one shown in Figure 3.2.8. Include in your design one tab for each pair of edges that must be glued together. Verify that your pattern works by constructing the tetrahedron.
4. Construct a pattern for an octahedron like the one shown in Figure 3.2.9. Include in your design one tab for each pair of edges that must be glued together. Verify that your pattern works by constructing the octahedron.
5. Construct a pattern for an icosahedron like the one shown in Figure 3.2.12. Include in your design one tab for each pair of edges that must be glued together. Verify that your pattern works by constructing the icosahedron.
6. Using a regular pentagon the size of the one shown below, construct a pattern for a dodecahedron. Include one tab in your design for each pair of edges that must be glued together. Verify that your pattern works by constructing the dodecahedron.

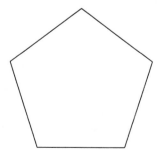

7. Using a square the size of the one shown below, design a pattern for a cube. Try to come up with a pattern different from the three given in Section 3.1 of the text. Include one tab for each pair of edges that must be glued together. Verify that your pattern works by constructing the cube.

In Exercises 8 and 9, seams must be included in the patterns rather than tabs.

8. Kathy Seaton wants to design a bean bag for her kid brother, Tommy. The bean bag will be rectangular and made from denim. Design a pattern for Tommy's bean bag.

9. Hans, an upholsterer, wants to cover an octagonal hassock with brown leather (see below). Design a pattern for Hans to use in cutting out the leather pieces.

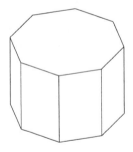

10. Estimate the amount of concrete necessary to construct the basement shown in the following floor plan:

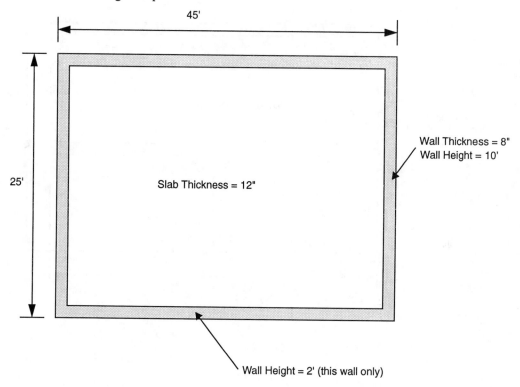

11. Estimate the amount of concrete necessary to construct the basement shown in the following floor plan:

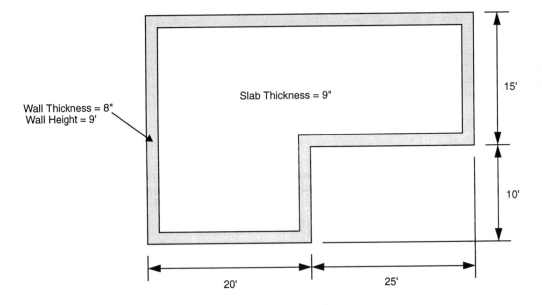

Slab Thickness = 9"

Wall Thickness = 8"
Wall Height = 9'

15'

10'

20'

25'

REFERENCES

HEATH, SIR THOMAS L. *The Thirteen Books of Euclid's Elements*, 2d ed. New York: Dover, 1956.

4

Coordinate Drawings

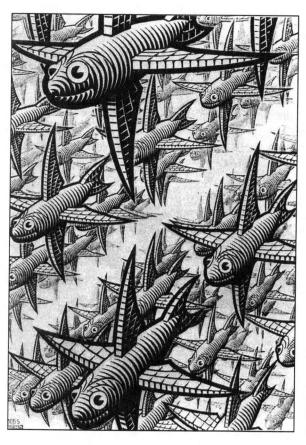

Mind teaser*: What aspects of this drawing make it appear 3-dimensional?

Answer: Fish that the artist wants to appear closer are made larger. The horizontal fins, vertical fins, and body of the fish give the picture length, height, and depth, respectively.

4.1 COORDINATE DRAWINGS OF 2-D FIGURES

Points on a planar figure require two coordinates to define their locations—an X-coordinate and a Y-coordinate. With the exception of points that lie on a coordinate axis (or axes), we say that points fall into one of four quadrants. Figure 4.1.1 shows the four quadrants of an XY-coordinate plane.

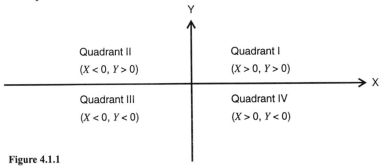

Figure 4.1.1

Orthographic views of a 3-D object can be sketched on an XY-coordinate plane using square dot or square grid paper. One nonvisual way to record the shape of a planar figure is to list the X-, Y-coordinates of the figure's corners as one traces around it. Generally speaking, one picks a point on the figure, somewhere near the middle, and calls it the origin of the XY-coordinate system.

Figure 4.1.2 shows a planar front view of a 3-D object, and Table 4.1.1 lists most of the coordinates needed to draw the view. In the exercises, you will be asked to fill in the missing coordinates of this table. Note that points E, F, G, H, and I lie in Quadrant I; point J lies in Quadrant II; and points C and D lie in Quadrant IV. Point A is at the origin of the XY-coordinate system, point K lies on the X-axis, and point B lies on the Y-axis.

Sometimes it is necessary to "move" from one point to a second point without drawing a line segment between them. This situation is recorded in the Move/Draw column as a 0; whereas, drawing a line segment between the two points is recorded as a 1. A zero opposite a point means that one arrived at that point from the previous point by "picking up" the pen and moving it there, rather than by drawing a line segment from the previous

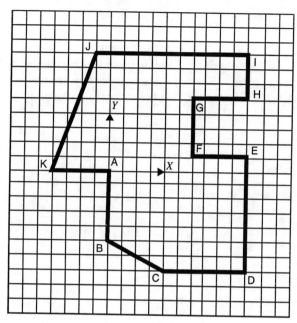

TABLE 4.1.1

Point	Coordinates X	Y
A	0	0
B	0	-5
C	?	?
D	10	-7
E	10	1
F	?	?
G	6	5
H	10	5
I	?	?
J	-1	8
K	?	?
A	0	0

Figure 4.1.2

point. Figure 4.1.3 and Table 4.1.2 show the use of the Move/Draw command in tracing out a rectangle with two diagonals. Note that moving from point C to point D the second time is accomplished without redrawing line segment $\overline{CD}$. This is desirable in computer drawing packages because lines drawn on top of lines can complicate later editing.

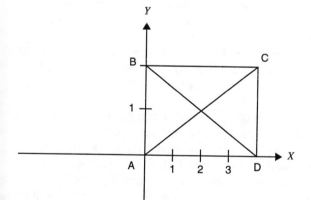

Figure 4.1.3

TABLE 4.1.2

Point	Move 0 Draw 1	Coordinates X	Y
A	0	0	0
B	1	0	2
C	1	4	2
D	1	4	0
A	1	0	0
C	1	4	2
D	0	4	0
B	1	0	2

EXERCISES 4.1

1. Fill in the missing coordinates for points C, F, I, and K in Table 4.1.1.
2. Draw the planar figure generated by plotting the points given in the table below on square grid paper and by drawing (or not drawing) a line segment between consecutive points as indicated by the Move/Draw command. Let point A serve as the origin of the XY-coordinate system.

Point	Move 0 Draw 1	Coordinate X	Y
A	0	0	0
B	1	0	2
C	0	−1	2
D	1	1	2
E	0	−4	3
F	1	−4	5
G	1	−3	4
H	1	−2	5
I	1	−2	3
J	0	2	−1
K	1	2	−3
L	1	4	−3
M	1	4	−1

4.2 3-D COORDINATE SYSTEMS

The *oblique* coordinate system and the *isometric* coordinate system are two different coordinate systems commonly used in drawing 3-dimensional objects. Most of the 3-D drawing you have done so far has been on isometric dot paper, so implicitly you have been using an isometric coordinate system. In 3-space, the X-axis, the Y-axis, and the Z-axis are all mutually perpendicular. However, the relationship of these axes on a 2-D surface, such as a piece of paper, is portrayed differently using isometric and oblique coordinate systems. Figure 4.2.1 shows the orientation of the coordinate axes in each of these systems.

It is important to be able to visualize the axes of these two coordinate systems as being mutually perpendicular in 3-space. With isometric axes, think of the X- and Z-axes as perpendicular to one another and lying together in a plane with the Y-axis perpendicular to that plane. With oblique axes, visualize the X- and Y-axes as perpendicular to one another lying in a plane with the Z-axis perpendicular to that plane. Figure 4.2.2 shows these two interpretations. In mathematics, almost all 3-D graphs are done using oblique axes, but engineers use both types of coordinate axes.

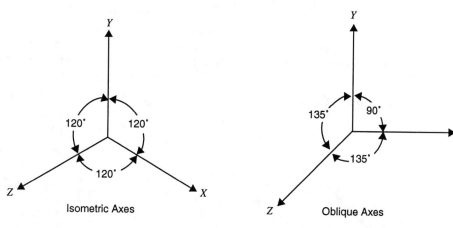

Figure 4.2.1

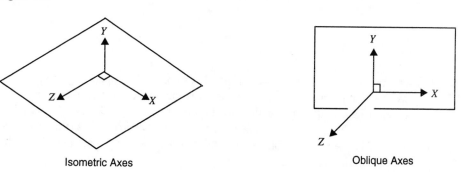

Figure 4.2.2

The actual labeling of axes may also differ depending on academic discipline and topic of discussion. Figure 4.2.3 shows two common labeling schemes of the X-, Y-, and Z-axes for an oblique coordinate system.

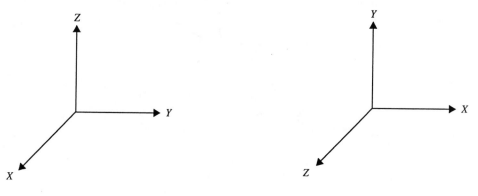

Figure 4.2.3

All of the coordinate systems discussed so far have axes that follow the *right hand rule*: If you place the fingers of your right-hand along the positive X-axis and rotate them in the direction of the positive Y-axis, then the thumb of your right hand will point in the direction of the positive Z-axis (see Figure 4.2.4). You will occasionally see a coordinate

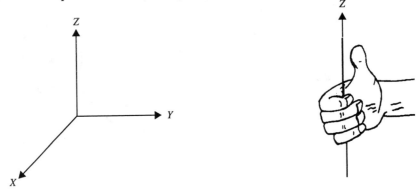

Figure 4.2.4

system labeled using the *left-hand rule*: If you place the fingers of your *left* hand along the positive X-axis and rotate them in the direction of the positive Y-axis, then the thumb of your left hand will point in the direction of the positive Z-axis. Figure 4.2.5 shows an isometric coordinate system labeled using the left-hand rule. In the next section, you will see both isometric and oblique coordinate systems being used, but all labeling will be done using the right-hand rule.

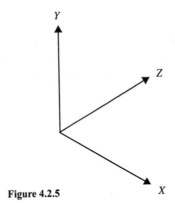

Figure 4.2.5

Isometric drawings represent true projections of objects. With isometric projection, the viewing plane is located perpendicular to a diagonal of a cube. However, drawing an object using an oblique coordinate system does not give a true projection of the object. For this reason, most computer software packages that represent 3-D views of objects use only the isometric projection scheme.

The main disadvantage of drawing with isometric projection is that all surfaces on the object will appear distorted, whereas with oblique drawing, one surface of the object appears in true shape and size. Figure 4.2.6 shows a cube drawn using both isometric and oblique coordinate systems.

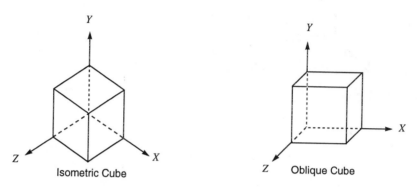

Isometric Cube

Oblique Cube

Figure 4.2.6

As can be seen in the isometric view of the cube, each face of the cube appears as a parallelogram, not as a square. In contrast, one face of the oblique drawing of the cube appears as a square, with the remaining surfaces as parallelograms. Thus, oblique drawing is sometimes preferred for objects that have a complicated surface, because the complex surface can be shown in true shape, with the remaining surfaces shown distorted. This is especially true when drawing single-curved surfaces. With isometric drawings, the curved surface will always appear as an ellipse. However, if an oblique drawing is made, it is possible to create the drawing so that the curved surface appears as a circle.

EXERCISES 4.2

In Exercises 1 to 4, identify each of the following coordinate axes as isometric or oblique and as right-handed or left-handed.

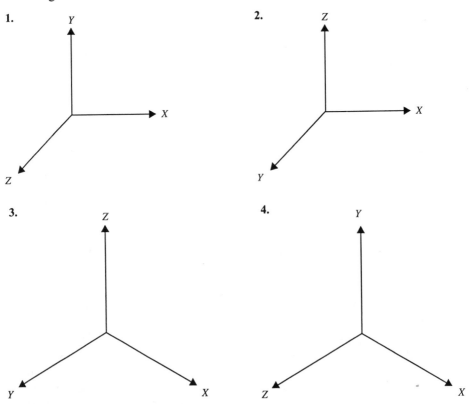

1.

2.

3.

4.

5. In Exercise 1, which axis should be visualized as being perpendicular to the plane of this page?

6. In Exercise 3, which axis should be visualized as being in the plane of this page?

4.3 COORDINATE DRAWINGS OF 3-D OBJECTS

If the three mutually perpendicular coordinate planes shown in Figure 4.3.1 are extended indefinitely, then we say they split 3-space into eight octants. It is easier to visualize these eight octants by confining 3-space to the volume inside an object, like a cube. If one positions the center of the XYZ-coordinate system inside the cube, as shown in Figure 4.3.2, then these coordinate planes divide the cube into eight smaller cubes, or octants.

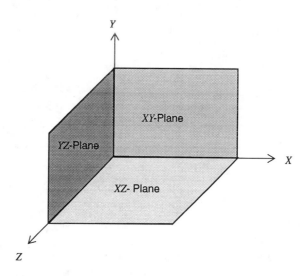

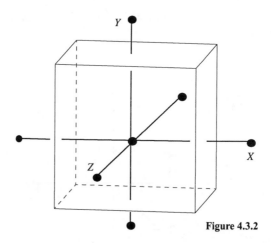

Figure 4.3.2

Points on a 3-D object require three coordinates to define their locations—an *X*-coordinate, a *Y*-coordinate, and a *Z*-coordinate. In the top four octants, the *Y*-coordinate of a given point is positive. In the bottom four octants, the *Y*-coordinate is negative. Figure 4.3.3 shows the top four octants. Octant V would be directly below Octant I, and for points in Octant V, *x* would be positive, *y* would be negative, and *z* would be positive. Similarly, Octants VI, VII, and VIII would be directly below Octants II, III, and IV, respectively.

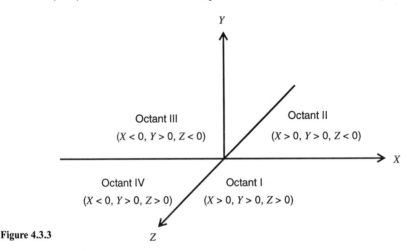

Figure 4.3.3

Plotting a three-coordinate point, P(*x*, *y*, *z*), is similar to plotting a two-coordinate point, P(*x*, *y*), except that, in addition to moving in the *X*- and *Y*-directions, one must also move in a third direction—the *Z*-direction. Figure 4.3.4 shows several points plotted in 3-space. Note that point P is in Octant II, point R is on the *XY*-coordinate plane, and point Q is in Octant VIII.

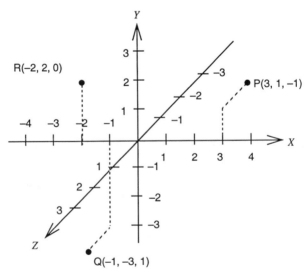

Figure 4.3.4

One way to draw a 3-D object is by plotting the corners of the object and then connecting pairs of corners with line segments. The corners are points in 3-space, and a Move/Draw command tells which points to connect with line segments. An isometric drawing of a 3-D object on isometric grid paper is shown in Figure 4.3.5. Note that on isometric grid paper, the X-, Y-, and Z-axes are oriented the same as they would be on isometric dot paper. Also note that in contrast to previous isometric drawings, the hidden

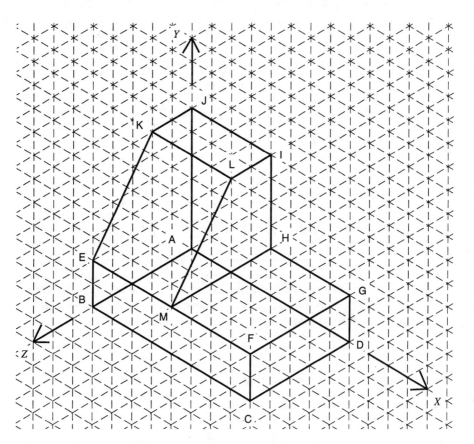

Figure 4.3.5

lines of the object are drawn and are represented by solid lines. By including hidden lines, the object is shown as a *wireframe*. Vertices of the object can now be assigned X-, Y-, and Z-coordinates. A partial listing of the vertices and their coordinates as one traces out the 3-D object are shown in Table 4.3.1. In the exercises, you will be asked to fill in the missing entries.

TABLE 4.3.1

Point	Move 0 Draw 1	X	Y	Z	Point	Move 0 Draw 1	X	Y	Z
A	0	0	0	0	I	1	4	6	0
B	1	0	0	5	L	0	?	?	?
C	1	8	0	5	M	1	4	2	5
D	1	8	0	0	K	0	0	6	2
A	1	0	0	0	E	1	0	2	5
B	0	0	0	5	J	0	0	6	0
E	1	0	2	5	A	1	0	0	0
F	1	8	2	5	M	0	4	2	5
G	1	?	?	?	H	1	4	2	0
H	1	4	2	0	F	0	8	2	5
I	1	4	6	0	C	1	8	0	5
J	1	0	6	0	G	?	?	?	?
K	1	0	6	2	D	?	8	0	0
L	1	?	?	?					

In some computer-aided modeling packages, one can enter the coordinates of two consecutive vertices of an object and connect those vertices with a line segment. This process can then be repeated until the entire object is defined.

It is important to note that our discussion of the X-, Y-, and Z-coordinate axes can be related to our previous discussion of orthographic and isometric views of an object. Each of the orthographic views can be thought of as the view of the object when looking down one of the coordinate axes. For example, an observer sees the top view of the object by looking down the Y-axis from a sufficient distance away. Similarly, the front view is obtained by looking down the Z-axis, and the right-side view by looking down the X-axis. This is illustrated in Figure 4.3.6. Isometric views of objects are obtained when the observer is somewhere along the line in space where $x = y = z$ and is far enough away from the object that it is entirely visible.

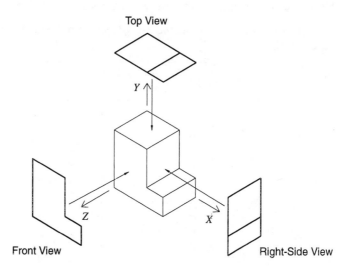

Figure 4.3.6

EXERCISES 4.3

1. Plot the following points on an oblique axis as shown in Figure 4.3.4. Label each point
   and name the octant or coordinate plane in which each point lies.

   A(3, 1, 4)   B(2, 1, –3)   C(1, –2, 0)   D(–4, 1, –2)
   E(0, 2, –1)   F(2, –3, 1)   G(3, –2, –1)   H(–4, –2, –1)
   I(2, 0, –1)

2. Complete the missing entries in Table 4.3.1 for vertices G and L and the missing
   Move/Draw commands for the last two vertices of the table.

3. On isometric grid paper, draw the 3-D object from the data given in the table below.
   Label each point.

Point	Move 0 Draw 1	X	Y	Z
A	0	0	0	0
B	1	0	3	0
C	1	0	4	4
D	1	0	1	4
E	1	1	0	3
F	1	2	0	0
A	1	0	0	0
D	1	0	1	4
C	0	0	4	4
E	1	1	0	3
B	0	0	3	0
F	1	2	0	0

4.4 APPLICATIONS

Land Surveying

Surveying has long been used in measuring and marking land for personal ownership. Ancient Babylonians and Egyptians used crude measurement devices to establish landmarks and distinguish different people's property. Nineteenth-century pioneers in the opening West measured their homesteads by pacing off specified distances. Surveying has evolved into an exacting science with precision instruments capable of measuring distances to the nearest thousandth of a foot and measuring angles to fractions of seconds. Unlike the homesteads, which were typically square or rectangular parcels of land, most property is not regularly shaped. When mapping out a parcel of land, a surveyor constructs what is known as a *traverse*. In surveying terms, a **traverse** is a multisided area of land that starts and stops at the same point. When taking field data for a traverse, the surveyor determines both the distance between the points that define the traverse and the bearing of each of the edges of the traverse. This information is then used in the computation of the area of the traverse. The mathematical technique used in calculating the area of the traverse is beyond the scope of this text, but sketching the traverse itself is possible using the techniques previously described in this chapter.

In analyzing the field data to complete an accurate drawing of the traverse, a **bearing** of a line is defined as the angle the line makes with a true north-south line. Figure 4.4.1 shows how bearings of lines are defined.

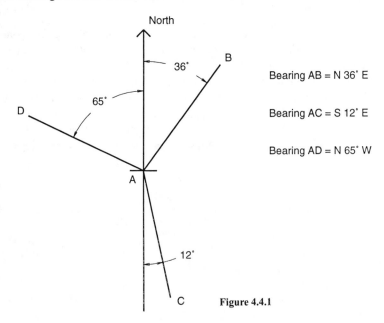

Figure 4.4.1

Figure 4.4.2 shows a typical five-sided traverse, and Table 4.4.1 gives the field data obtained by the surveyor.

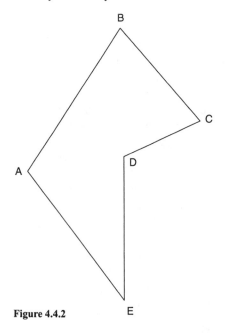

Figure 4.4.2

TABLE 4.4.1

Side	Length	Bearing
AB	236.2 ft	N 34.2° E
BC	168.8 ft	S 41.3° E
CD	117.5 ft	S 65.6° W
DE	198.3 ft	due south
EA	224.9 ft	N 37.5° W

If A is considered to be the origin of the coordinate system, going from point A to the opposite endpoint of any given line changes both x and y. Changes in the north and east directions are analogous to positive changes of x and y; changes in the south and west directions are analogous to negative changes of x and y. The amount of change in x and y between point A and point B is related to the length and the bearing of the line AB. Specifically, the change in x is equal to the length of the line multiplied by the sine of the bearing, and the change in y is equal to the length of the line multiplied by the cosine of the bearing. This is illustrated in Figure 4.4.3. In surveying terminology, changes along the

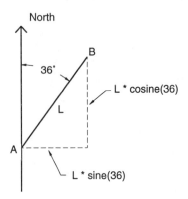

Figure 4.4.3

east-west line (changes in x) are called **departures**, and changes along the north-south line (changes in y) are called **latitudes**. When compiling traverse data, it is important to note that the sum of all of the departures as well as the sum of all of the latitudes must equal zero, because a traverse begins and ends at the same point. The departures and latitudes from traverse data are also used to determine the X-, Y-locations of the points around the traverse. Table 4.4.2 shows the data obtained from the traverse in Figure 4.4.1.

TABLE 4.4.2

Line	Length	Bearing	Departure + East	Departure − West	Latitude + North	Latitude − South
AB	236.2 ft	N 34.2° E	132.7		195.3	
BC	168.8 ft	S 41.3° E	111.3			126.8
CD	117.5 ft	S 65.6° W		107.1		48.5
DE	198.4 ft	due south				198.4
EA	224.9 ft	N 37.5° W		136.9	178.4	
		Sums	244.0	−244.0	373.7	−373.7

Note that the sums of the latitudes and departures are indeed equal to zero, which indicates that the surveyor started and stopped at the same point. If point A is selected as the origin for the traverse, the X- and Y-coordinates of the subsequent points in the traverse equal the cumulative sum of the departures and latitudes, respectively, up to the point under consideration. Thus, for point C, the X-coordinate is equal to the departure for AB plus the departure for BC, or $132.7 + 111.3 = 244.0$. (The Y-coordinate is equal to the sum of the latitudes, i.e., $195.3 − 126.8 = 68.5$). Table 4.4.3 includes the X- and Y-coordinates for each of the points in the traverse.

TABLE 4.4.3

Point	X	Y
A	0.0	0.0
B	132.7	195.3
C	244.0	68.5
D	136.9	20.0
E	136.9	−178.4
A (check)	0.0	0.0

Electrical Conduits

In designing a new building, an electrical engineer must see that power is distributed throughout the building in a logical manner. Typically, the power source is distributed vertically through the building, and then electrical conduits connect horizontally to the source on the floors of the building. Sometimes a piece of equipment on one of the floors has significant power needs. A separate conduit might be located on the floor just for that piece of equipment.

It is useful to be able to visualize how power is distributed throughout a building. One can then determine the shortest path for future wiring projects. One also can determine whether there are unnecessary cables in the building if any area of the building has too many conduits.

Because the power source is a vertical line through the building, it is useful to think of it as extending along the Y-axis. The power conduits that are connected to the source then extend in the X- and Z-directions. For example, consider a five-story building approximately 50 feet in height. If one plots the main power source for the building. and uses a scale of one grid point equal to 10 feet, the drawing shown in Figure 4.4.4 results.

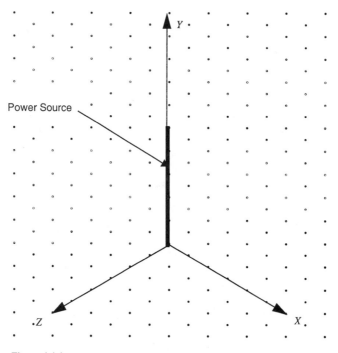

Figure 4.4.4

In this case, the conduit lines all begin at the power source and extend in the X- and Z-directions. Therefore, the starting point of each conduit line occurs at a given Y-value, and the beginning X- and Z-values are both zero. The ending point for each conduit line is at the same Y-value as the starting point, but at different X- and Z-values. Each conduit that extends from the power source can then be plotted as lines in 3-space. For example, Table 4.4.4 contains the locations of the conduit lines for this building. To plot the first

TABLE 4.4.4

Conduit Line	Y-Location	Endpoint X-Location	Z-Location
A	0'	0'	30'
B	10'	40'	0'
C	10'	20'	30'
D	20'	10'	20'
E	30'	30'	10'
F	40'	40'	0'
G	50'	40'	0'
H	50'	0'	30'

conduit line (A), start at the Y-location on the power source and drawn a line to the point $x = 0$, $y = 0$, $z = 30$. Recall that the distance between grid points is equal to 10 feet. When conduit A is included, the drawing should look like that shown in Figure 4.4.5.

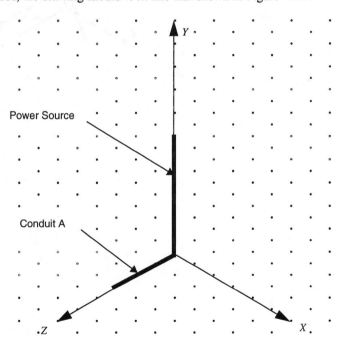

Figure 4.4.5

Figure 4.4.6 shows the electrical power supply diagram when all of the conduits have been included. Each conduit is labeled in the figure.

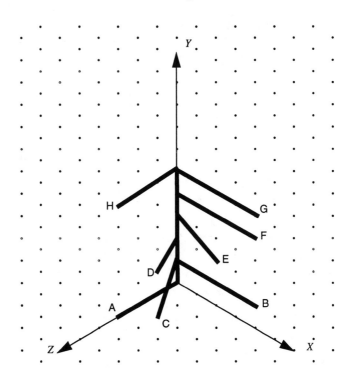

Figure 4.4.6

EXERCISES 4.4

1. Determine the *X*- and *Y*-coordinates of each of the points A-E in the traverse shown below. For the latitudes and departures to sum exactly to zero, you may have to adjust some of the values (error is due to round-off in the data). Make all changes to line EA so that the departures and latitudes sum to zero.

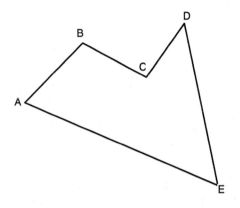

Line	Length	Bearing
AB	263.4 ft	N 44.3° E
BC	227.9 ft	S 62.0 ° E
CD	207.1 ft	N 35.3° E
DE	518.4 ft	S 11.9° E
EA	663.8 ft	N 67.2° W

2. Determine the *X*- and *Y*-coordinates of each of the points A-F in the traverse shown below. You may have to adjust some of the latitudes and departures to make them sum to zero (error is due to round-off). Using small square grid paper, with one grid square equal to 20 feet, plot the traverse. Count the number of squares inside the traverse to estimate the traverse area.

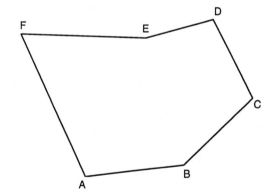

Line	Length	Bearing
AB	234.2 ft	N 83.4° E
BC	223.0 ft	N 46.8° E
CD	203.0 ft	N 27.7° W
DE	164.0 ft	S 74.9° W
EF	296.9 ft	N 88.3° W
FA	360.0 ft	S 25.3° E

3. Draw the power source and conduit lines for a building according to the following specifications. The building height is 40 feet. Use a grid spacing of one grid space equals 5 feet. The power source line extends along the Y-axis from the origin to a height of 40 feet. The conduit lines are defined in the following table. Label each conduit line in your drawing.

| Conduit Line | Y-Location | Endpoint | |
		X-Location	Z-Location
A	0'	20'	0'
B	10'	20'	15'
C	10'	25'	5'
D	20'	10'	0'
E	20'	30'	10'
F	30'	5'	25'
G	40'	10'	25'
H	40'	20'	0'

4. Draw the power source and conduit lines for a building according to the following specifications. The building height is 70 feet. Use a grid spacing of one grid space equals 10 feet. The power source line extends along the Y-axis from the origin to a height of 70 feet. The conduit lines are defined in the following table. Label each conduit line in your drawing.

| Conduit Line | Y-Location | Endpoint | |
		X-Location	Z-Location
A	0'	40'	50'
B	10'	30'	60'
C	20'	0'	50'
D	30'	20'	40'
E	40'	50'	0'
F	50'	50'	20'
G	60'	0'	40'
H	70'	30'	50'

5

Transformation of 3-D Objects

Mind teaser*: Which geometric transformation (translation, scaling, rotation, or reflection) is used in the picture?   *Answer:* Reflection.

A geometric **transformation** of a solid is a one-to-one mapping of the points of a first solid object into the points of a second solid object. The second solid is called the **image** of the first under a given transformation. There are four types of geometric transformations that we will consider: a *translation*, a *dilation* (or scaling), a *rotation*, and a *reflection*. The rotation is the most difficult of the four geometric translations to visualize, so the greatest amount of time will be spent on it.

5.1 TRANSLATION OF OBJECTS

A geometric **translation** of an object is the sliding of the object in the *X*-, *Y*-, or *Z*-direction or in a combination of these directions. Figure 5.1.1 illustrates the translation of an object in each of these directions. Essentially, a translation takes place when an object is "picked

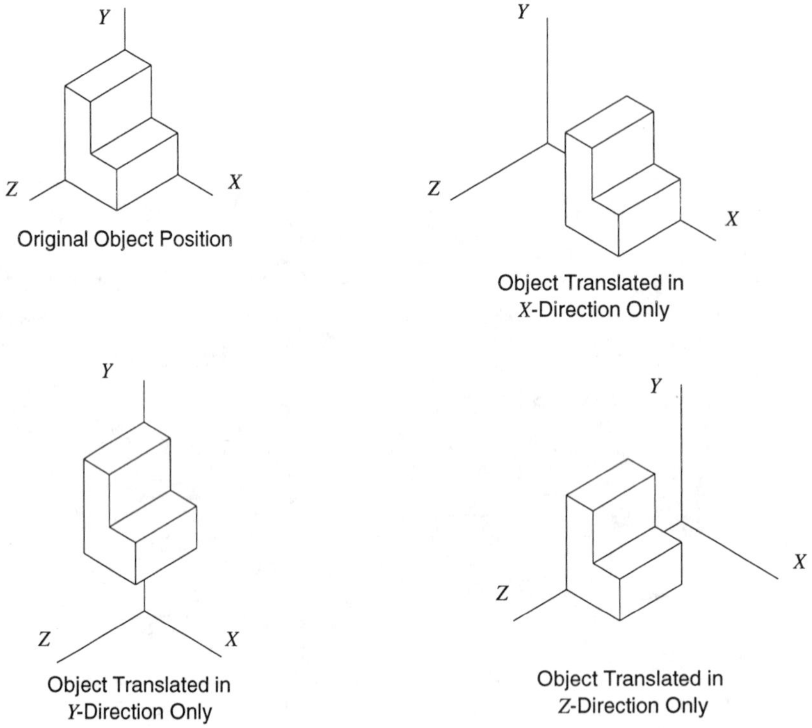

Original Object Position

Object Translated in
X-Direction Only

Object Translated in
Y-Direction Only

Object Translated in
Z-Direction Only

Figure 5.1.1

up" from one location and is moved to a new location without any turning of the object or physical changes to its shape. The image is merely the original object in a new location. In a translation, the isometric and orthographic views of the image are identical to the corresponding views of the object. The edges of the object that started out parallel to the *X*-axis remain parallel to the *X*-axis after the object is moved; edges originally parallel to the *Y*-axis remain parallel to the *Y*-axis after the move; and edges originally parallel to the *Z*-axis remain parallel to the *Z*-axis after translation. Figure 5.1.2 shows complete engineering layouts of an object before and after translation. Notice that they are identical.

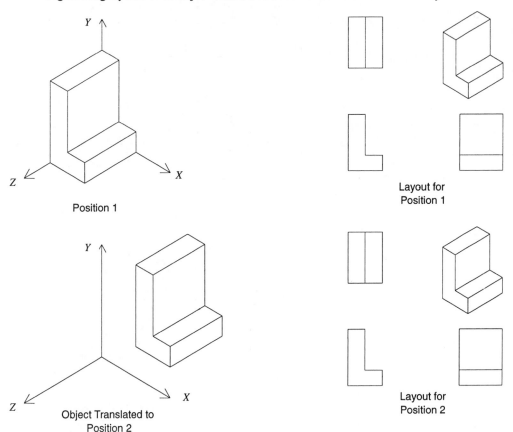

Figure 5.1.2

Isometric dot paper enables one to be more quantitative about the translation of objects. Consider the L-shaped object shown in Figure 5.1.3. If it is translated 1 unit in the *X*-direction, −3 units in the *Y*-direction, and 2 units in the *Z*-direction (1, −3, 2), where is the image? One approach to solving this problem is to move critical points, e.g., vertices of the object, and then use the images of these points to sketch a total image of the object. This is possible because each point undergoes the same translation that the solid as a whole experiences (e.g., A→A′, B→B′, C→C′, and D→D′). Similarly, the edges of the solid undergo the same translation (e.g., $\overline{AB} \to \overline{A'B'}$ and $\overline{CD} \to \overline{C'D'}$). The final image of the L-shaped solid in Figure 5.1.3 is shown in Figure 5.1.4.

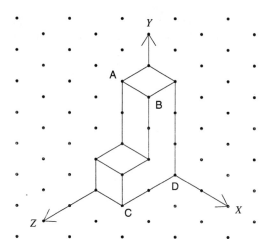

Figure 5.1.3

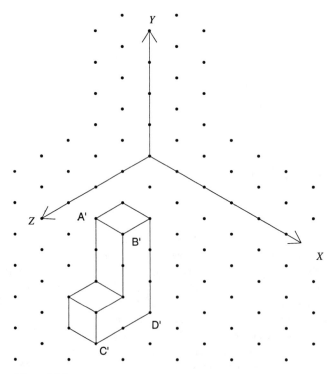

Figure 5.1.4

When one uses isometric dot paper to make object translations, one must note the *X*-, *Y*-, and *Z*-coordinates of the critical point on the object. Because isometric grid paper is a 2-D representation of 3-D space, each dot on the grid paper can represent more than one location in space. For example, point A shown in Figure 5.1.5 can have several possible 3-D coordinates which describe it. Possible coordinates for this point include: (–2, 0, 0), (0, 2, 2), (1, 3, 3), or (2, 4, 4). In reality, one is looking down a line in space and "seeing" the end view of the line. Thus, each grid point represents an end view of a line in space rather than a single point. For this reason, one must note the coordinate location of the critical point to make the proper object translation.

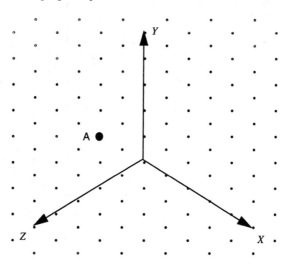

Figure 5.1.5

EXERCISES 5.1

In Exercises 1-6, translate the object shown below as indicated in each exercise. Draw the image of each object after translation on isometric dot paper. On each drawing, indicate the location of the X-, Y-, and Z-coordinate axes.

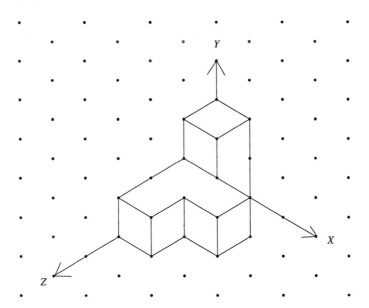

1. Translate the object 2 units in the X-direction.

2. Translate the object –3 units in the Y-direction.

3. Translate the object 1 unit in the Y-direction and 2 units in the Z-direction.

4. Translate the object –3 units in the X-direction and 2 units in the Y-direction.

5. Translate the object (4, –1, 2).

6. Translate the object (–1, 3, –2).

7. What translation would be required to move the object shown next from its current location to a new location where point A would lie on the X-axis, point B would lie on the Y-axis, and point C would lie on the Z-axis? Assume that point A currently has coordinates (5, 0, –2).

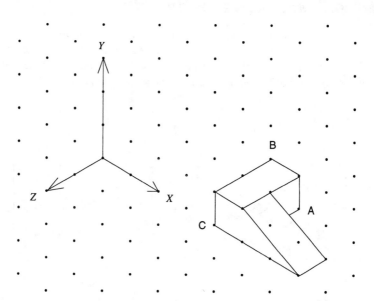

8. What translation would be required to move the cross shown below from its current location to a new location where point A would lie on the *X*-axis, point B would lie on the *Y*-axis, and point C would lie on the *Z*-axis? Assume point B currently has coordinates (–5, 1, 1).

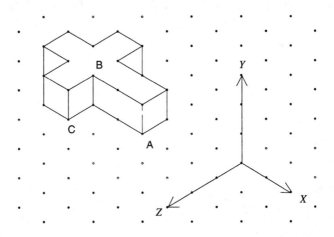

9. A 4-dimensional cube is called a **hypercube**. One way mathematicians propose visualizing a fourth dimension is by using a geometric transformation like translation. To draw a hypercube, draw a cube and its image after translation. Connect corresponding vertices with line segments (i.e., $\overline{AA'}$, $\overline{BB'}$,...). The result is one model of a hypercube. Draw a hypercube using this model.

5.2 DILATION (OR SCALING) OF OBJECTS

A geometric **dilation** (or scaling) of an object with a a multiplier $r \neq 1$ is an enlargement of the object if $r > 1$ and a shrinking of the object if $r < 1$. Consider the unit cube on the left in Figure 5.2.1. A dilation of the cube with $r = 3$ appears at the right. We say that the cube is enlarged or *scaled up* by a **factor** (or multiplier) of 3.

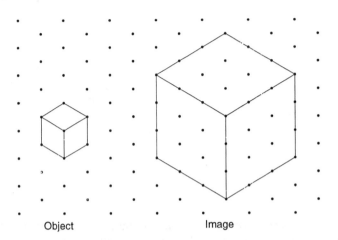

Figure 5.2.1   Object   Image

Isometric and orthographic views of the object and image after scaling are similar but not identical. Complete engineering drawings of the unit cube and its enlarged image ($r=3$) are shown in Figure 5.2.2. In this case, the object and the image are relatively true in size.

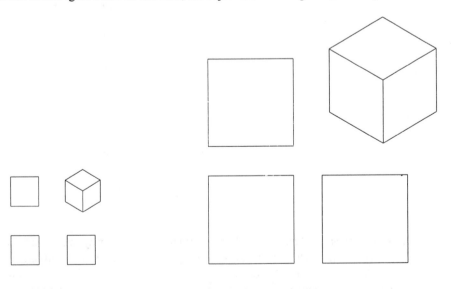

Figure 5.2.2   Object   Image

There are many objects that are similar in shape but different in size. Dry cereal boxes are one example. A Corn Flakes™ box with $12'' \times 9'' \times 3''$ dimensions would be similar in shape to a Grape Nuts™ box with $8'' \times 6'' \times 2''$ dimensions. In this case, the Grape Nuts™ box could be regarded as a Corn Flakes™ box scaled down by a factor of ⅔. Pieces of clothing or pairs of shoes that come in different sizes but the same style illustrate a practical application for scaling objects in the retail world.

In engineering, there are two predominant uses of the word scale. The first use is as a synonym for dilation, which means that the true size of the object is different from the true size of its image. Figure 5.2.3 illustrates this use of the word *scale*. From the lengths of the line segments, one can tell that the object at the left has been dilated (or scaled up) by a factor of 2 to produce the image at the right.

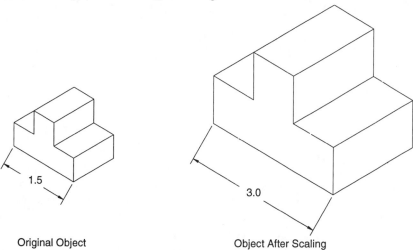

Original Object   Object After Scaling

Figure 5.2.3

The second and more prevalent use of the term *scale* in engineering is where the object is drawn so that it does not appear in its true size on paper. This is known as drawing an object to scale. By drawing objects to scale, engineers, architects, and city planners are able to communicate their designs to one another and to the people who construct the objects. Imagine how difficult it would be to design a building effectively if the architect were only able to draw it at its true size. A piece of paper would have to measure 50 feet × 100 feet or bigger. Figure 5.2.4 illustrates this use of the word *scale*. Here

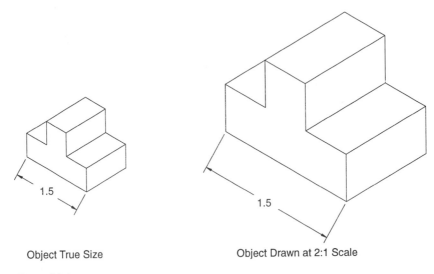

Object True Size　　　　　　　　　　　　Object Drawn at 2:1 Scale

Figure 5.2.4

the objects are the same size: The one on the right just appears to be twice as large as the one on the left. The notation of a 2:1 scale means that 2 inches on paper equal 1 inch on the object. The drawing therefore looks larger than the actual object. Conversely, a 1:2 scale would mean that 1 inch on paper represents 2 inches on the physical model; hence, the drawing would look smaller than the actual object. In denoting scales, the first number in the ratio corresponds to the drawing, and the second number in the ratio corresponds to the physical object.

　　　Another way to think of drawing objects to scale is that the scale merely indicates how close one is to the object. If one is a substantial distance from the object, it appears very small; whereas, if one is very close to the object, it appears large. However, the true object size does not change. Similarly, from an airplane, a house on the ground looks tiny, but if one is standing a few inches from the same house, it appears enormous. Clearly, it is the perception of the house that changes, not the size of the house.

　　　The concept of drawing an object to scale has previously been illustrated in this text in our discussion of surveying traverses. Figure 4.3.2 shows a traverse that in reality measures hundreds of feet, but on the page it measures only a few inches. Scales for drawings are usually reported as ratios, as discussed previously. However, sometimes drawing scales are given with an equal sign rather than a ratio. This is particularly true when scales are given in the English system of units. Thus, a scale may be reported as 1" = 50', or ¼" = 20'. These drawing scales can be related back to their ratio equivalents, i.e., 1" = 50' corresponds to a scale of 1:600 (there are 12 inches in a foot), and a scale of ¼" = 20' corresponds to 1:960.

EXERCISES 5.2

1. A triangular prism is shown below. Reduce the prism to ⅓ its current size, and make a complete engineering drawing of the reduced image. (The orthographic views can be done on square dot paper and the isometric view on isometric dot paper.)

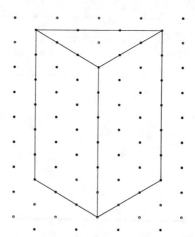

2. Another way that mathematicians visualize a hypercube is by use of dilation, as shown below. The hypercube consists of the original cube as well as its image after dilation. Corresponding vertices of the two cubes are connected by line segments. Draw the three orthographic views of this hypercube. Try to draw an isometric view. Why is this difficult?

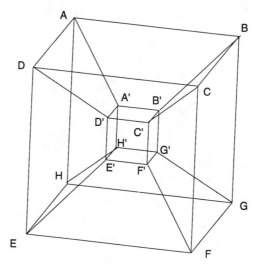

3. Why is drawing an object to scale (as shown in Figure 5.2.4) *not* a transformation of the object?

4. The line below is drawn at a scale of 1:6. Measure the line with a ruler. What value is the dimension on the actual line? Your answer may be given either in inches or in centimeters.

5. The rectangle shown below is drawn at a scale of 3:2. Measure the sides with a ruler in inches. What are the dimensions of the actual rectangle?

6. For a scale of 1" = 1 mile, what is the scale expressed as a ratio?

7. For a scale of 1" = 30', draw a line that represents an actual line of length 120'.

8. Draw a rectangle whose dimensions are 4" × 6" at a scale of 1:2.

5.3 *ROTATION OF OBJECTS ABOUT A SINGLE AXIS*

A geometric **rotation** of an object is a turning of the object about a straight line that is referred to as the **axis of rotation**. In this section, we will discuss rotations occurring about a single axis, such as the X-, Y-, or Z-axis.

Imagine a door as it is moved from a position of closed to open, and let the vertical line along which the hinges lie be called the Y-axis (see Figure 5.3.1). As the door is

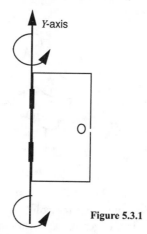

Figure 5.3.1

pushed inward from a position of closed to a position of open, it is said to rotate about the Y-axis. Note that in rotating a 3-D object, the object remains in contact with the axis of rotation. If initially one is looking at the front of the door, then after a 90° counterclockwise rotation, one will be looking at an edge of the door. Figure 5.3.2 shows orthographic views of a door before and after rotation about the Y-axis.

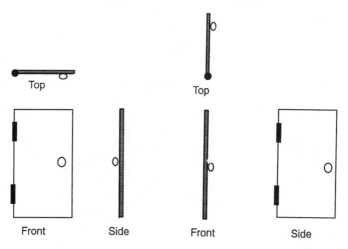

Figure 5.3.2   Door in Closed Position   Door in Open Position

The direction of rotation of a solid object is determined by the right-hand rule. If the thumb of your right hand points along the axis of rotation, then your fingers will curl in the direction that the object rotates. In the case of the door that rotates about its hinges (shown in Figures 5.3.1 and 5.3.2), the thumb of your right hand points in the positive Y-direction, and the fingers of your right hand curl in the direction the door rotates (see Figure 5.3.3).

Figure 5.3.3

Figure 5.3.4 illustrates the rotation of a solid about each of the X-, Y-, and Z-axes. In each case, it should be noted that the solid object remains in contact with the axis of rotation. One of the object edges remains stationary, while the rest of the object pivots about the axis. This is in contrast to the case of translation of solid objects where none of the object edges remains in its original position.

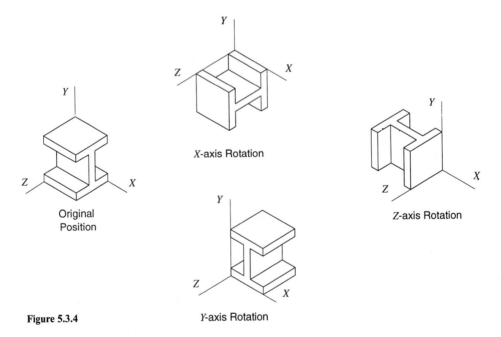

Figure 5.3.4

An object can rotate in two directions about an axis. If the thumb of the right hand is pointed along the positive direction of an axis, then the fingers of the right hand curl in one direction. We will call such object rotation a **positive (or counterclockwise) rotation**. In contrast, if the thumb of the right hand is pointed along the negative direction of an axis, then the fingers of the right hand curl in the opposite direction. We will call such object rotation a **negative (or clockwise) rotation**. Figure 5.3.5 illustrates a positive as well as a negative rotation of an object about the X-axis.

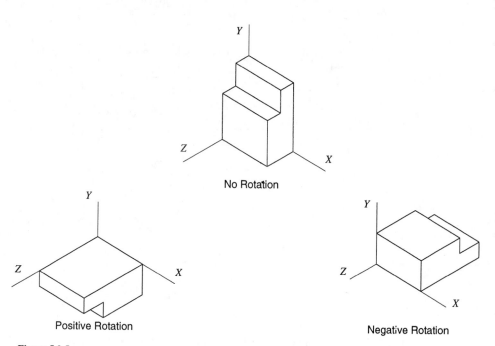

Figure 5.3.5

Another difference between the rotation and the translation of solids is that rotation will significantly change the appearance of the object in each of its orthographic views as well as in its isometric view. With rotation of solids about an axis, the edges originally parallel to the axis of rotation remain parallel after movement. However, the edges of the object parallel to axes other than the axis of rotation are no longer parallel to those same axes. This results in orthographic and isometric views of the object unlike those of the object in its original position. Figure 5.3.6 illustrates the rotation of an object about the Y-axis and the corresponding drawing layouts for the two orientations.

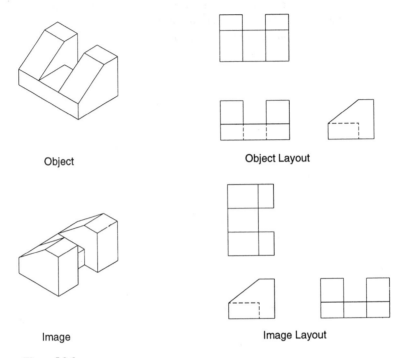

Object   Object Layout

Image   Image Layout

Figure 5.3.6

The following arrow coding scheme, can be used to record the actual rotation(s) an object has experienced. Let a single arrow to the right (⟶) represent a 90° positive rotation, a double arrow to the right (⟹) represent a 180° positive rotation, a single arrow to the left (⟵) represent a 90° negative rotation, and so on. The axis of rotation is then indicated to the right of the arrow(s). Therefore, the notation (⟶ Y) would represent a 90° positive rotation about the Y-axis.

Imagine a unit cube constructed from the flat pattern shown in Figure 5.3.7. We will choose an original position for the cube that exposes the faces lettered C, U, and H, and

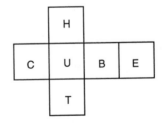

Figure 5.3.7

then perform various rotations about the Y-axis. A sampling of possible rotations and the arrow coding of these rotations are shown in Figure 5.3.8. The rotation in part c is a 270° negative (clockwise) rotation about the Y-axis and is equivalent to the 90° positive (counterclockwise) rotation shown in part a.

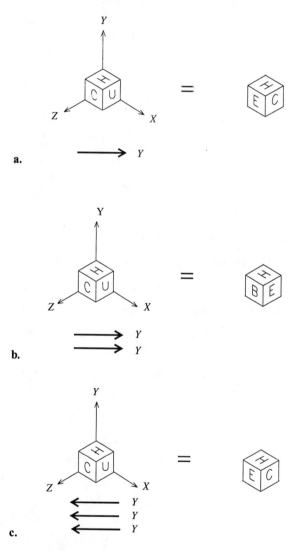

Figure 5.3.8

EXERCISES 5.3

In Exercises 1 to 4, rotate the object below as indicated; draw the object in its final position on isometric dot paper; and indicate the arrow coding of the rotation below your drawing.

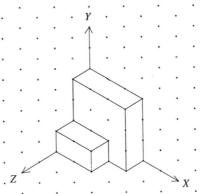

1. A negative 90° rotation about the X-axis.

2. A positive 90° rotation about the Z-axis.

3. A positive 90° rotation about the Y-axis.

4. A positive 270° rotation about the Y-axis.

5. Draw the orthographic views of the object in Exercise 1 before and after rotation. Are the orthographic views the same or different?

6. Draw the orthographic views of the object in Exercise 2 before and after rotation. Are the orthographic views the same or different?

In Exercises 7 to 8, describe in writing and with arrow coding what rotation the object has experienced about the indicated axis. Express each answer using as few arrows as possible.

7.

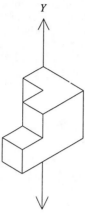

Initial Position

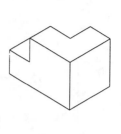

Final Position

8.

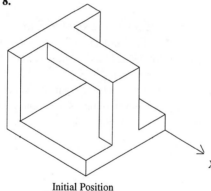

Initial Position

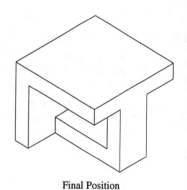

Final Position

In Exercises 9 to 12, indicate whether the object rotations are equivalent.

9. $\begin{pmatrix} \longrightarrow Z \\ \longrightarrow Z \\ \longrightarrow Z \end{pmatrix} = \begin{pmatrix} \longleftarrow Z \end{pmatrix}$

10. $\begin{pmatrix} \longrightarrow X \\ \longrightarrow X \end{pmatrix} = \begin{pmatrix} \longleftarrow X \end{pmatrix}$

11. $\begin{pmatrix} \longleftarrow Y \\ \longleftarrow Y \end{pmatrix} = \begin{pmatrix} \longrightarrow Y \\ \longrightarrow Y \end{pmatrix}$

12. $\begin{pmatrix} \longleftarrow X \\ \longrightarrow X \\ \longrightarrow X \end{pmatrix} = \begin{pmatrix} \longleftarrow X \end{pmatrix}$

5.4 ROTATION OF OBJECTS ABOUT TWO OR MORE AXES

In the same manner that objects are rotated about a single axis, they can be rotated about two or more axes in a series of steps. In Figure 5.4.1, an L-shaped object has a 90° negative

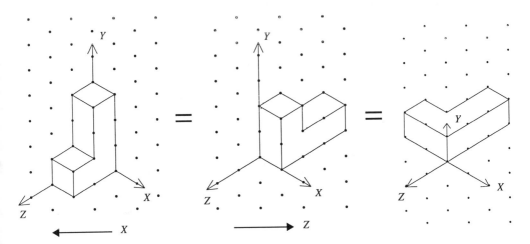

Figure 5.4.1

rotation about the X-axis, followed by a 90° positive rotation about the Z-axis. The arrow coding for such a two-step rotation would be ($\overset{X}{\underset{Z}{\longleftrightarrow}}$). Figure 5.4.2 shows an object that has had a 90° negative rotation about the X-axis, followed by a 90° positive rotation about the Y-axis. The arrow coding for this two-step rotation would be ($\overset{X}{\underset{Y}{\longleftrightarrow}}$). When a rotation occurs about a single axis, an entire edge remains in its original position. When rotations occur about two different axes, only a single pivot point remains stationary. In Figures 5.4.1 and 5.4.2, this single pivot point is the origin ($x=0, y=0, z=0$).

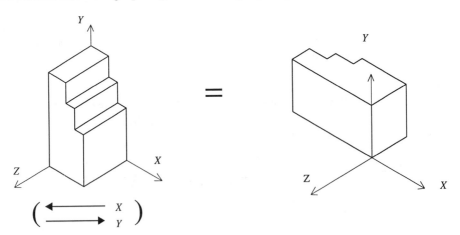

Figure 5.4.2

When a solid rotates about two different axes, the final location and orientation of the solid depend on the order in which the rotations are performed. That is, rotation of a solid about two different axes is not commutative. The commutative property fails because the object edges originally parallel to an axis are no longer parallel to that same axis after rotation. Figure 5.4.3 illustrates the failure of the commutative property to hold in object rotation about two different axes. In the first case, the original object was rotated about the X-axis and then about the Y-axis.

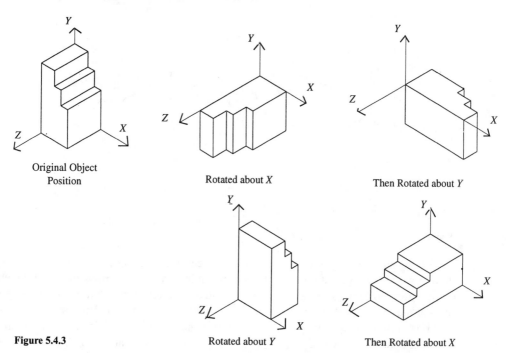

Original Object Position   Rotated about X   Then Rotated about Y

Figure 5.4.3   Rotated about Y   Then Rotated about X

The arrow coding for this rotation is ($\longrightarrow {}^X_Y$). In the second case, the original object was rotated about the Y-axis and then about the X-axis. The arrow coding for this rotation is ($\longrightarrow {}^Y_X$). Note that in these two cases the two objects' final locations and orientations are different.

An object can be rotated about as many axes as one wishes. For example, an object rotation with the arrow coding

$$\begin{pmatrix} \longrightarrow X \\ \longrightarrow Z \\ \longrightarrow Z \\ \longleftarrow Y \end{pmatrix}$$

means that the original object has a 90° positive rotation about the X-axis; then a 180° positive rotation about the Z-axis; and, last of all, a 90° negative rotation about the Y-axis. The L-shaped object shown in Figure 5.4.4 has experienced this set of rotations while going from its original position to its final position.

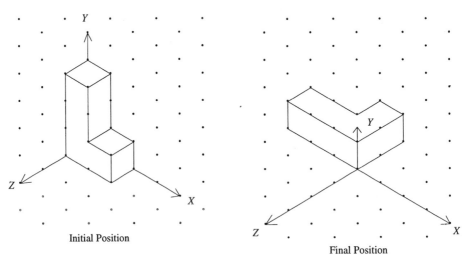

Initial Position

Final Position

Figure 5.4.4

A set of object rotations about two or three axes can sometimes be reduced to a simpler set of object rotations (i.e., the arrow coding has fewer arrows in it, but the end result is the same). It is not always easy to find a simpler set of rotations. One needs to concentrate on the initial and final positions of the object and find the shortest set of rotations between these two positions. A simpler set of object rotations for the rotation shown in Figure 5.4.4 would be ($\xrightarrow{Z}\xleftarrow{X}$), a 90° positive rotation about the Z-axis followed by a 90° negative rotation about the X-axis.

EXERCISES 5.4

In Exercises 1 to 4, rotate the solid below as indicated. Then, on isometric dot paper, draw the object in its final position relative to the *X*-, *Y*-, and *Z*-axes, and indicate the arrow coding of the rotation below your drawing.

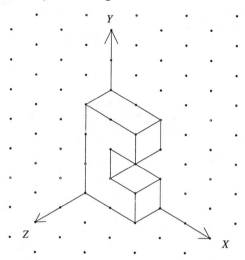

1. A positive 90° rotation about the *X*-axis followed by a positive 90° rotation about the *Z*-axis.

2. A negative 90° rotation about the *X*-axis followed by a positive 180° rotation about the *Y*-axis.

3. A positive 180° rotation about the *Z*-axis followed by a positive 90° rotation about the *Y*-axis.

4. A negative 90° rotation about the *Z*-axis followed by a positive 180° rotation about the *X*-axis.

In Exercises 5 to 8, study how the object on the top line is rotated. (*Hint:* It may be helpful to identify the axis of rotation or to devise a coding scheme for the rotation.) Then rotate the object below it in the same manner, and draw the second object in its final position on isometric dot paper.

5.

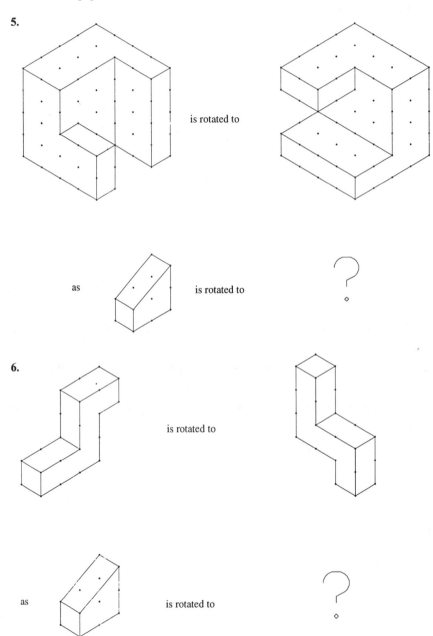

7.

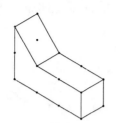   is rotated to

as   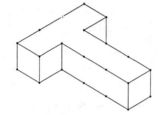   is rotated to

8.

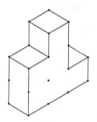   is rotated to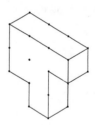

as   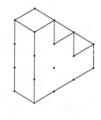   is rotated to

9. Rotate the object shown below as indicated by the arrow coding

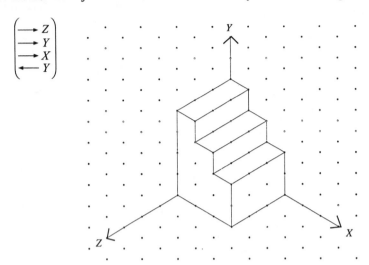

Find a simpler set of object rotations to achieve the final position of the object. Express your answer using arrow coding. Are other answers possible?

10. Rotate the object shown below as indicated by the arrow coding.

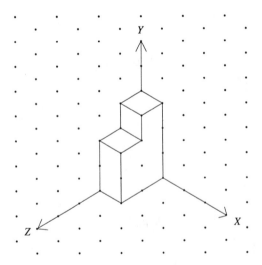

a. ($\Longrightarrow^{Y}_{Z}$) Draw the rotated object on isometric dot paper.

b. ($\Longrightarrow^{Z}_{Y}$) Draw the rotated object on isometric dot paper.

c. Compare your answers for parts a and b. Is object rotation commutative?

5.5 REFLECTION OF OBJECTS

A geometric **reflection** of an object across a plane P is a geometric transformation that associates each point A of the object with an image point A' in the reflection such that plane P is a perpendicular bisector of the line segment $\overline{AA'}$. (*Note:* If a point of the object lies on plane P, then it is its own reflection.) Figure 5.5.1 shows two different objects and their reflections across plane P. Plane P is technically not a mirror but a plane about which the object is being reflected. Hence, the image of the reflection and the original object are located on opposite sides of plane P.

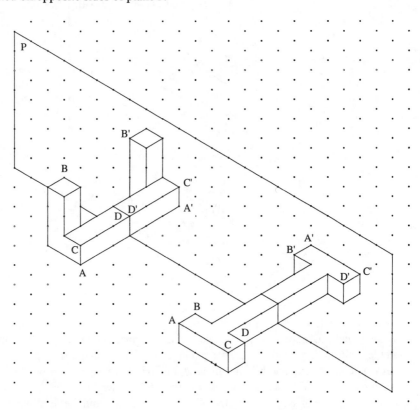

Figure 5.5.1

A 3-D object is said to be **symmetrical** if a plane can cut the object such that the part of the object on the left side of the plane is the reflection of the part of the object on the right side of the plane (or vice versa). In Figure 5.5.1, the T-shaped object is symmetrical, but the other object is not. Figure 5.5.2 shows the T-shaped object being cut by plane Q

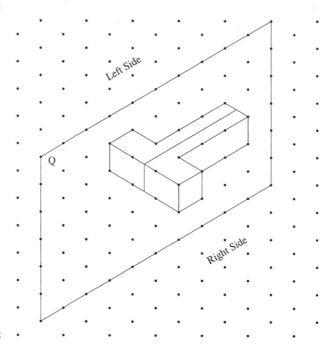

Figure 5.5.2

such that the left side of the object is a reflection of the right side of the object. For symmetrical 3-D objects, it is possible to use two rotations to achieve the same effect as a single reflection, provided that the plane of symmetry and the plane of reflection are perpendicular to one another. In this case, the axis of rotation must be the line formed by the intersection of these two planes. Figure 5.5.3 shows the reflection of a symmetrical object, the plane of symmetry Q, the plane of reflection P, and the resulting axis of rotation. Figure 5.5.4 shows the object in Figure 5.5.3 experiencing two positive 90° rotations about the axis of rotation. Notice that the images of the object after the geometrical transformations of reflection (Figure 5.5.3) and rotation (Figure 5.5.4) are the same.

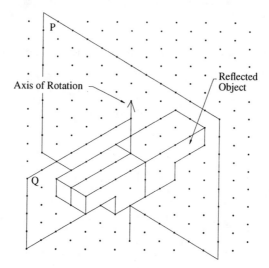

Figure 5.5.3

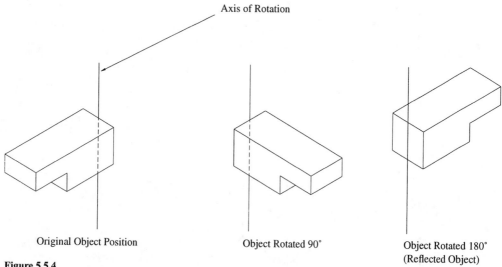

Original Object Position   Object Rotated 90°   Object Rotated 180°
                                                                                                (Reflected Object)

Figure 5.5.4

EXERCISES 5.5

In Exercises 1 to 4, copy plane P on a piece of isometric dot paper, and draw the reflection
of the given object.

1.

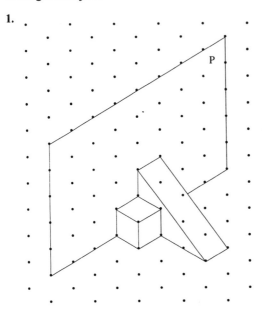

2.

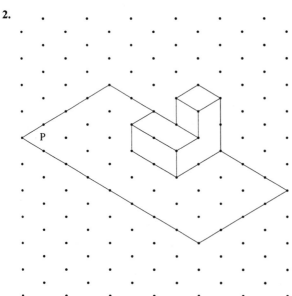

3.

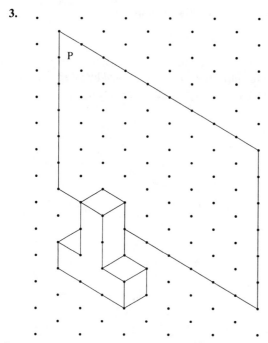

Note: This object is located 2 units away from the plane P.

4.

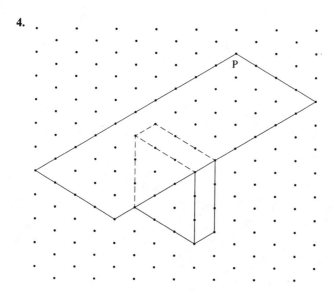

5. How many planes of symmetry does the object pictured in Exercise 3 have?

6. How many planes of symmetry does the object pictured in Exercise 4 have?

7. On isometric dot paper, copy plane P and the T-shaped object. Draw the reflection of the object about plane P. Can the reflection be accomplished by an equivalent set of two 90° rotations? If so, draw the axis of rotation in its proper location.

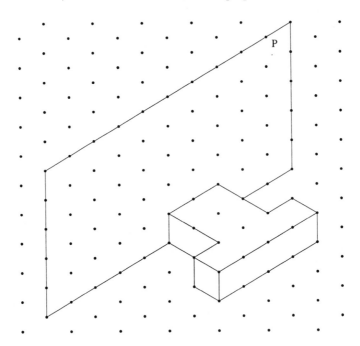

5.6 APPLICATIONS

Chemistry

Stereoisomers are classified by chemists as molecular compounds or ions that have the same molecular formula and the same order of attachment but different orientations of their atoms. Stereoisomers are further divided into two categories based on how their atoms are oriented in 3-space: conformational isomers and configurational isomers (Brown). We will discuss conformational isomers and configurational isomers both because they do not require a high level of chemistry expertise and because they are obvious applications of ideas developed in this chapter.

Conformational isomers of a simple compound differ only by a rotation of atoms about a single bond. A molecule such as ethane (CH_3—CH_3) has many different conformations. One can visualize these different conformations by pretending to hold one CH_3 group and twisting the other CH_3 group about the single bond joining the two carbon atoms. Figure 5.6.1 shows one conformation of ethane represented in three different ways. Figure 5.6.1a is a ball-and-stick model of one view of this conformation. In this model, the sticks from the hydrogen atoms to the carbon atom are all the same lengths, but some look shorter than others due to their orientation. (Recall our discussion in Section 2.3 about inclined surfaces appearing foreshortened in orthographic projections.) Figure 5.6.1b is another ball-and-stick model of the same conformation but rotated in 3-space, so it is being viewed from a different angle. Note that the three hydrogen atoms are equally distributed about the carbon atom in each CH_3 group. Figure 5.6.1c is a *Newman projection* of Figure 5.6.1b looking "head on" at the ethane compound down the C—C bond. Because the hydrogen atoms around the first and second carbon atoms are oriented differently in this projection (60° apart), it is referred to as the *staggered* conformation of ethane.

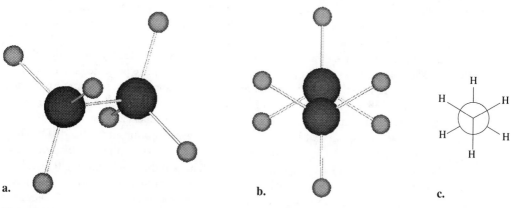

Figure 5.6.1

Figure 5.6.2 shows a second conformation of ethane. Basically, the CH_3 group in the staggered conformation of ethane in Figure 5.6.1 has been rotated 60° about the C—C bond (the axis connecting the two carbon atoms) to create the conformation shown in Figure 5.6.2a. Note that in Figure 5.6.2b, the hydrogen atoms on the back carbon atom are

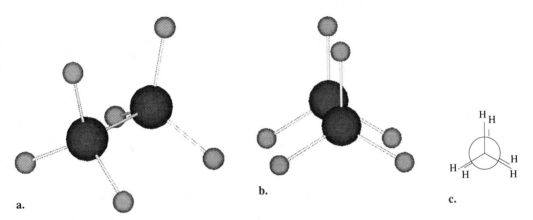

a.   b.   c.

Figure 5.6.2

lined up with the hydrogen atoms on the front carbon atom. For this reason, we find it hard to see the back CH_3 group when looking "head on" down the C—C bond. Consequently, this conformation is called the *eclipsed conformation*. Figure 5.6.2c shows the *Newman projection* of the eclipsed conformation. Conformations of ethane such as the two shown in Figures 5.6.1. and 5.6.2 are interconvertible (i.e., capable of switching between one another). At room temperature, ethane molecules not only move around within the container holding them but also undergo rapid internal rotation about the C—C bond.

Some stereoisomers exhibit unusual optical properties. Isomers that are *optically inactive* will not rotate plane polarized light when it is passed through a solution containing the isomer. In contrast, the stereoisomers in the next category we will discuss (configurational isomers) are optically active and will rotate plane polarized light.

Technically speaking, **configurational isomers** are isomers whose atoms are oriented in 3-space in such a way that they are nonsuperimposable on their mirror images (or reflections). Objects that are nonsuperimposable with their reflected images are said to be **chiral** (rhymes with spiral and is derived from a Greek word meaning "handed"). These isomers are said to share the same nonsuperimposable property with their reflections that a right hand shares with a left hand. The fact that a right hand and a left hand are nonsuperimposable is easily shown by trying to put a right-hand glove on a left hand. Isomers with the common property of chirality share many other properties: the same melting point, the same boiling point, and the same solubilities in certain solvents. Yet they may differ in how they rotate plane polarized light. One isomer may rotate it in one direction ("left" for counterclockwise and "right" for clockwise), while the other rotates it the same amount but in the opposite direction (Mortimer).

Lactic acid is one example of a molecule that is not superimposable on its mirror image. Lactic acid was first isolated from sour milk in 1780 and later from muscle tissue in 1807. It is the acid generated in human muscles that causes them to feel sore after strenuous exercise. Figure 5.6.3 shows a ball-and-stick model of a lactic acid molecule at the left and its mirror image at the right. Note that there is no way the molecule at the left can be picked up, turned in space, and placed directly on top of the molecule at the right. Hence, lactic acid is a nonsuperimposable molecule and is optically active. In fact, only two of the four groups attached to the central carbon atom can be made to coincide, as long as no bonds are broken.

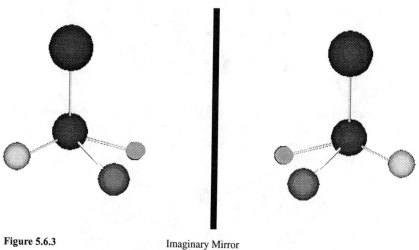

Figure 5.6.3   Imaginary Mirror

Crystallography

The science of crystallography uses the three geometric transformations of translation, rotation, and reflection. The invariance (lack of change) of crystals under these transformations accounts for the symmetrical beauty of crystals.

Translational symmetry is basic to the definition of a crystal. For example, the unit cell for a salt (NaCl) crystal is comprised of sodium and chlorine ions. Figure 5.6.4.shows a ball-and-stick model of a unit cell of an NaCl crystal. Crystals can be thought of as being built up by translation of its fundamental building block, the unit cell.

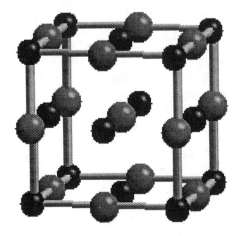

Figure 5.6.4

René Haüy (1742–1822), the "father of crystallography," theorized that for a given mineral, any of its varied crystal shapes could be constructed by the appropriate stacking of unit cells with the same orientation. Figure 5.6.5 shows unit cells being stacked together

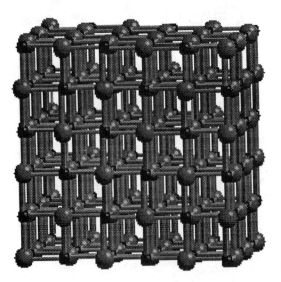

Figure 5.6.5

with the same orientation to form the sodium chloride crystal. This regular stacking of the unit cells of a crystal accounts for the flat faces so often associated with crystals. Note, for example, the flat triangular faces of tetrahedrite crystals from Romania in Figure 5.6.6.

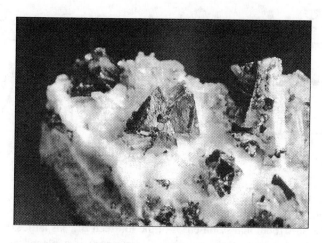

Figure 5.6.6

In a crystal, each unit cell has the same surroundings as every other unit cell, and if one imagines a point, such as the center of the cell, representing the position of the unit cell, then this set of regularly spaced points is called a **lattice**. Using the fact that each point in a lattice has the same surroundings as every other point, Auguste Bravais (1811–1863) showed that there are only fourteen different lattices in 3-space.

Classification of crystals is based in part on their rotational and reflectional symmetries. Christian Weiss (1780–1856) and Frederich Mohs (1773–1839) set up classifications based on the invariance of crystals under the transformations of rotation and reflection.

"A crystal has **rotational symmetry about an axis** (an imaginary line through the center of the crystal) if it repeats itself in appearance one or more times as it is rotated one complete revolution about that axis"(Jaszczak, p. 87). Crystals are classified according to the number of times the crystal repeats itself on rotation about an axis of rotation. For example, a crystal with three-fold symmetry will repeat itself in appearance three times when rotated 360° about a three-fold axis, four times when rotated 360° about a four-fold axis, and so on. Gold forms a cubic crystal which has three four-fold axes, four three-fold axes and six two-fold axes. Figure 5.6.7 illustrates these different symmetry axes within a

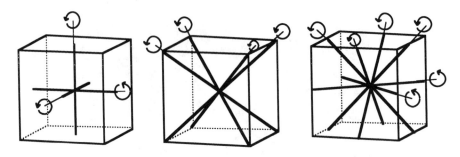

Figure 5.6.7

cubic shape. Because by definition, crystals are composed of a stacking of identical unit cells, only one-fold, two-fold, three-fold, four-fold and six-fold symmetry axes are allowed. These are the only rotational symmetries of the fourteen Bravais lattices.

"A crystal has **reflection** (or mirror) **symmetry** if a plane can be found which divides the crystal into two halves which are mirror images of each other" (Jaszczak, p. 87). Figure 5.6.8 shows the six mirror planes of the cubic crystal of gold, each perpendicular to one of its six two-fold axes. Two of the cubes have the two-fold axis

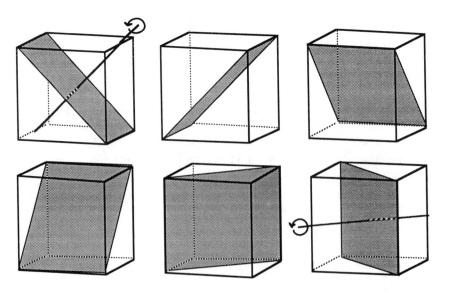

Figure 5.6.8

perpendicular to the mirror plane indicated. The location of the two-fold axes on the remaining four cubes is left as a homework exercise. Figure 5.6.9 shows the three mirror planes of gold, each perpendicular to one of its three four-fold axes.

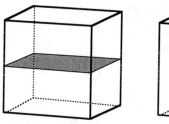 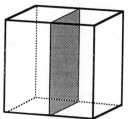 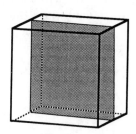

Figure 5.6.9

Other symmetry operations besides rotation and reflection can be derived by combining these two transformations into a single operation (e.g., an inversion symmetry is a two-fold or 180° rotation followed by a reflection through a plane perpendicular to the rotation axis). Various minerals possess different groupings of these symmetry operations, and it is these groupings that dictate which Platonic shapes are possible shapes for crystals. The tetrahedron, the cube, and the octahedron turn out to be possible shapes, but the dodecahedron and the icosahedron are not possible crystal shapes. In the 1800s Johann Hessel and Auguste Bravais each proved that only thirty-two different symmetry groupings are possible, and today these different groupings are known as the thirty-two crystal classes (Buerger, 1956).

EXERCISES 5.6

1. Below is a ball-and-stick model of butane (structural formula CH_3—CH_2—CH_2—CH_3).
   Draw a *Newman projection* of the eclipsed conformation. The arrow to the lower left of
   the ball-and-stick model indicates the appropriate viewing direction for the eclipsed
   conformation.

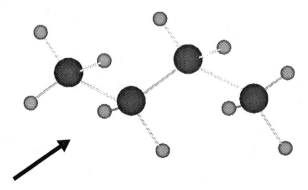

2. Below is a ball-and-stick model of glycine and an imaginary reflecting mirror.

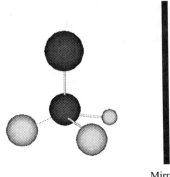

Mirror

   a. Draw a reflection of the glycine molecule to the right of the mirror.
   b. Is the glycine molecule superimposable on its reflected image (i.e., Can the glycine
      molecule at the left be picked up, turned in space, and placed directly on top of its
      reflection)?
   c. What can be said about glycine and its potential for optical activity?

3. Shown below is a regular tetrahedron, a form commonly assumed by the minerals tetra-hedrite and sphalerite. Copy the tetrahedron as many times as necessary to draw all the n-fold axes of rotational symmetry (i.e., draw one tetrahedron with all the two-fold axes and another tetrahedron with all the three-fold axes). How many axes are there for each kind of rotational symmetry?

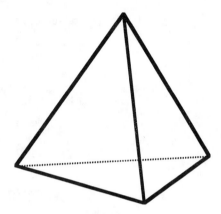

4. Draw all the six mirror planes of a regular tetrahedron. Draw each plane on a separate tetrahedron.

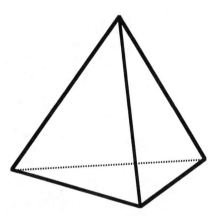

5. On Figure 5.6.8, locate the axes of rotation that are perpendicular to the indicated mirror planes. Note that on two of the cubes, axes are already drawn. Draw similar axes on the remaining four cubes.

REFERENCES

BROWN, WILLIAM H. *Introduction to Organic Chemistry,* 3d ed. Boston: Willard Grant Press, 1982.

BUERGER, M. J. *Elementary Crystallography.* New York: John Wiley & Sons, 1956.

JASZCZAK, J. A. Quasicrystals: Novel Forms of Solid Matter. *The Mineralogical Record* 25 (1994): 85–93.

MORTIMER, C. E. *Chemistry,* 5th ed. Belmont: Wadworth, 1983.

6

Cross Sections of
3-D Objects

*Mind teaser**: Does this picture demonstrate a cross section?

Answer: No. This is a spiral cut, not a planar cut. Only planar cuts create cross sections.

If a plane cuts a 3-D object, the **cross section** or face of the cut depends on how the plane is oriented relative to the object. We will see in Section 6.2 that some of the possible cross sections of a plane intersecting a cube are a triangle, a square, a pentagon, and a hexagon. The actual cross section that results depends on the angle at which the plane intersects the cube. Similarly, the shape of the intersection of a plane with other 3-D objects depends on how the plane is oriented relative to the object. Therefore, our first concern will be the correct naming and graphing of planes in 3-space.

6.1 GRAPHING OF PLANES IN 3-SPACE

The easiest planes to name and graph in 3-space are the coordinate planes and planes parallel to them. Figure 6.1.1 shows the three coordinate planes and their respective

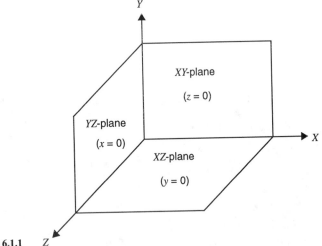

Figure 6.1.1

equations. In 2-space, an equation like $y=0$ means that the y-coordinate is always zero, but the x-coordinate has no constraint on it, or is said to be "free to vary." Hence, the equation $y=0$ in 2-space is a line. In particular, it is the X-axis. Similarly, the equation $y=2$ in 2-space is a line parallel to the X-axis but elevated two units in the positive Y-direction. In 3-space, the equation $y=0$ means that the y-coordinate is always zero, but the x-coordinate and the z-coordinate are both free to vary. Hence, in 3-space, the equation $y=0$ is the XZ-plane, and the equation $y=2$ would be a plane parallel to the XZ-plane but elevated two units in the positive Y-direction. Figure 6.1.2 shows the graph of the plane $y=2$, as well as the graphs for the planes $x=-4$ and $z=3$. These planes, although they appear finite in size, are theoretically infinite.

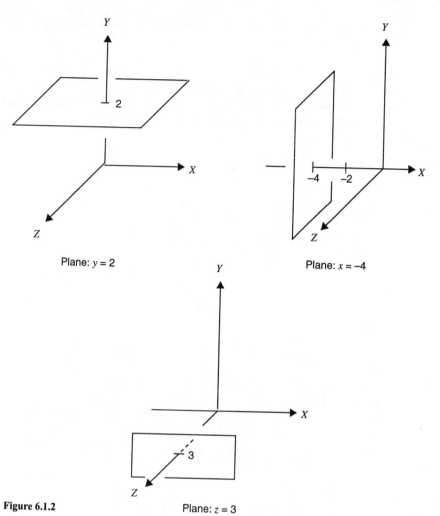

Figure 6.1.2

Plane: $y = 2$

Plane: $x = -4$

Plane: $z = 3$

There are some rules about drawing lines and planes that are important to follow for effective visual communication. Notice that when one draws planes parallel to the coordinate planes, they are drawn as parallelograms with sides parallel to the coordinate axes. Further notice that portions of the coordinate axes hidden by the planes either are not drawn (as in the graphs of $y=2$ and $x=-4$) or are drawn using dotted lines (as in the graph of $z=3$). Both practices are common and acceptable. It is also common practice not to let the axis line touch the boundary of the parallelogram, unless the axis line itself lies in the plane.

Planes that are not coordinate planes (or parallel to coordinate planes) will eventually intersect two or all three of the coordinate axes. The points where a plane intersects the X-, Y-, and Z-axes are called its "x-, y-, and z-**intercepts**," respectively. Provided that the equation for the plane is given, these intercepts are easy to find. (*Note:* The general equation for a plane in 3-space is $ax+by+cz=d$ where a, b, c, and d are real numbers.) To find the x-intercept, set $y=z=0$ in the equation of the plane. Along the X-axis, y and z are both 0, so the x-intercept will occur at the point on the plane where y and z take on the value 0. Similarly, the y-intercept can be found by setting $x=z=0$ and the z-intercept by setting $x=y=0$. Then graphing is as simple as connecting the three intercepts with line segments. Figure 6.1.3 shows the graph of the plane $2x+3y+4z=12$. The x-intercept occurs when $2x+3(0)+4(0)=12$ or at $x=6$. Similarly, the y-intercept occurs when $2(0)+3y+4(0)=12$ or at $y=4$, and the z-intercept occurs when $4z=12$ or at $z=3$.

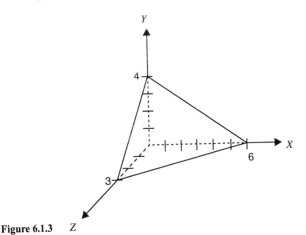

Figure 6.1.3   Z

Some equations for planes have only two variables. These equations look like the equations for lines in 2-space, but because they are being graphed in 3-space, they are actually planes. The missing third variable is free to vary, so the line slides in the direction of that variable, creating a plane. For example, the plane $3x+2y=6$ can be graphed as a line in the XY-plane with an x-intercept of 2 and a y-intercept of 3. Sliding the line along the Z-direction creates the graph of the plane (see Figure 6.1.4).

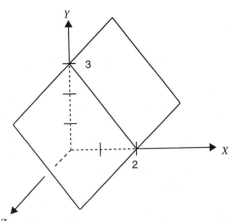

Figure 6.1.4   Z

EXERCISES 6.1

1. Examine the graphs shown below and answer the following questions.

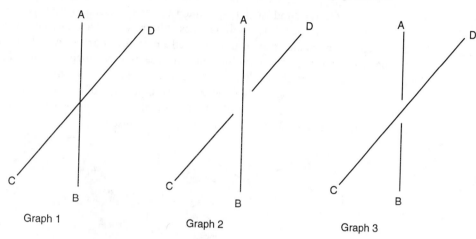

Graph 1

Graph 2

Graph 3

  a. In which graph does $\overline{AB}$ lie behind $\overline{CD}$?
  b. In which graph does $\overline{AB}$ cross $\overline{CD}$?
  c. In which graph does $\overline{CD}$ lie behind $\overline{AB}$?

2. Draw three different graphs of a plane and a line. The relationships between the plane and the line for each graph are described below.
   a. The line lies below the plane.
   b. The line lies in the plane.
   c. The line lies above the plane.

3. Graph the planes $z = 4$ and $z = -4$ on an XYZ-coordinate system.

4. Graph the planes $x = 3$ and $y = 4$ on an XYZ-coordinate system, showing their line of intersection.

5. Graph the plane with an x-intercept of 3, a y-intercept of –2, and a z-intercept of 1.

6. Graph the plane $2x - y + 5z = 10$.

7. Graph the plane $3y+5z=15$. *Hint:* $3y+5z=15$ can be graphed as a line in the YZ-plane, which slides in the X-direction to create a plane. This is because x is free to vary.

6.2 CUTTING PLANES AND CROSS SECTIONS

Cross-sectional views of a 3-D object are achieved by a plane intersecting the object and splitting it into two pieces. Planes that split objects into two pieces are called **cutting planes**. In Figure 6.2.1, a solid block is split into two parts by a cutting plane, and the front part of the block is removed. The resulting cross section is the shaded shape shown in the last picture. In this case, the cross section is called a **planar region** because the object was solid; whereas, if the object were hollow, the cross section is called a **planar figure**. A planar figure has only boundary lines, but a planar region includes the area inside the boundary lines as well. Regardless of whether the object is hollow or solid, the shape formed by the boundary lines of the cross section is the cross section's most interesting feature, and therefore will be the focus of the rest of this discussion.

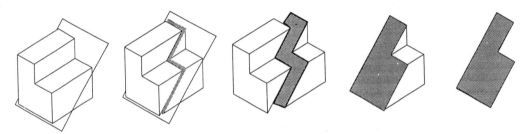

Figure 6.2.1

Figure 6.2.2 shows some planar figures that can result from different cutting planes intersecting a hollow cube. As you can see, the cross section that results depends on the orientation of the plane relative to the cube. In these cases, we mentally visualize the cross section formed by each cutting plane and draw it without physically splitting the cube into two parts.

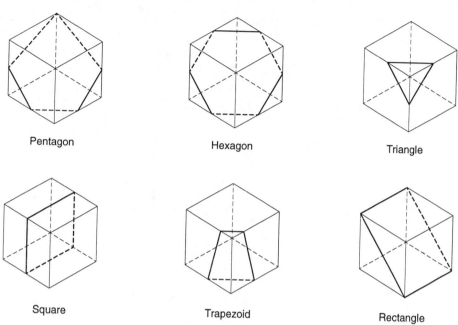

Pentagon   Hexagon   Triangle

Square   Trapezoid   Rectangle

Figure 6.2.2

Figure 6.2.3 shows a right circular double cone graphed on an *XYZ*-coordinate system. Possible cross sections of this double cone include a circle, an ellipse, a parabola, and a hyperbola. For this reason, these four geometric figures are often referred to as *conic sections*.

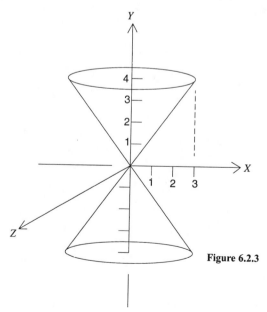

Figure 6.2.3

Figure 6.2.4 shows the intersection of a plane with the equation $x = 2$ and the double cone shown in Figure 6.2.3. The resulting cross section is a hyperbola. Drawing the intersection of planes with other orientations and the double cone shown in Figure 6.2.3 will be left for the exercises at the end of this section.

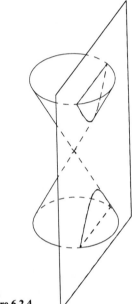

Figure 6.2.4

EXERCISES 6.2

In Exercises 1–4, draw the resulting cross section when the indicated cutting plane splits the solid object into two pieces. Shade the planar region included in the cross section.

1.   **2.**   **3.**   **4.**

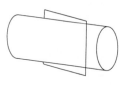

5. Draw the intersection of a plane with the equation $z=3$ with the double cone shown in Figure 6.2.3. Name the cross section.

6. Draw the intersection of a plane with the equation $y=-2x+2$ and the double cone shown in Figure 6.2.3. Name the cross section.

7. Below is a drawing of a right circular cylinder graphed on an XYZ-coordinate system. Draw and describe the cross sections formed by intersecting the following planes with the cylinder.

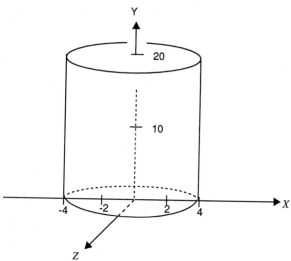

a. The XY-plane ($z=0$)
b. The XZ-plane ($y=0$)
c. The plane $x=2$
d. The plane $2x+4y+2z=8$

8. Below is an isometric drawing of a 3-D object. Assume that the dots along each axis are 1 unit apart. Draw on square dot paper and describe the cross sections formed by intersecting the following planes with the object.

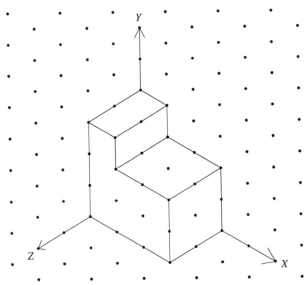

a. plane $y=1$
b. plane $x=2$
c. plane $z=1$

6.3 APPLICATIONS

Architecture

Frequently, blueprints for a house or other structure will feature cross-sectional views as well as orthographic views. These views enable a person to visualize what the structure will look like from many different perspectives. For buildings, the drawings with which you are probably most familiar include floor plans and elevation views. **Floor plans** show the layout of the individual rooms on each floor within the structure as seen from above. **Elevation views** typically appear as artists' renderings of what the building will look like from the outside after it is completed. Elevation views usually show the building from either a north, south, east, or west perspective. These two types of drawings are probably the most important drawings from the standpoint of selling a design to a prospective buyer, but from the standpoint of the contractor who will actually build the structure, they are probably among the least important.

Cross-sectional views are used to show the contractor exactly how the parts of the building fit together so it can be built effectively. For example, Figure 6.3.1 shows a vertical cross-section for a proposed house. This view has been drawn as if a vertical slice has been cut through the home. This vertical cross-section shows how the individual floors and rooms line up with one another.

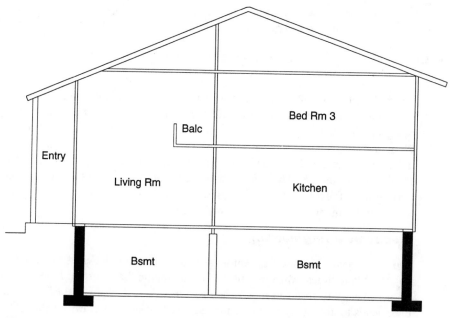

Figure 6.3.1

Cross-sectional views such as the one shown in Figure 6.3.1 are useful in showing the overall building and how its floors fit together, but a more common use for cross-sectional views in architectural drawing is to show details on how the various parts fit together. Detailed sectional views show just a small part of a building that would not typically be visible at the drawing scale used for the entire building. For example, in a floor plan for a personal home, the scale may be $\frac{1}{4}$" = 1' (scale = 1:48). But a detailed view for the same home might be drawn at a scale of 1:6, so that all of the individual features are readily distinguishable. Figure 6.3.2 shows a detailed cross-sectional view of

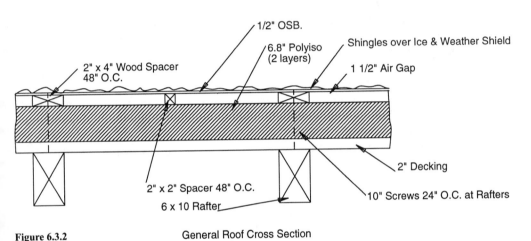

Figure 6.3.2   General Roof Cross Section

the roof section for the home shown in Figure 6.3.1. This detailed cross-sectional view depicts how the layers of the roof will be assembled to achieve the results specified by the designer. Note that for this particular roof, the 6×10 rafters support the roof, followed by 2" of decking. The insulation (6.8" Polyiso) lies on top of the decking. An air gap is achieved by placing 2×4's and 2×2's as spacers. These are covered by $\frac{1}{2}$" of OSB and, finally, by the shingles. This detail drawing conveys to the contractor at a glance what took a paragraph of text to describe. Also, if one knows how to read the drawings, there is often less room for misinterpretation than with the written word.

Mechanical Engineering

Cross-sectional views are frequently used on engineering drawings to show the interior of objects. Many times, when the rules of orthographic drawings are followed, a given view of the object will result in mostly hidden lines. An excess of dashed lines on a drawing often leads to ambiguity or confusion. Sectional views are drawn to show the interior of an object so that hidden lines can be avoided.

In making sectional views, part of the object is "cut" away and the resulting interior is exposed. As the plane cuts through the object, part of the plane will pass through material, and part will not. Cross-hatching is added to the object in the areas where the cutting plane encounters material. For example, Figure 6.3.3 shows the orthographic views for a hollowed-out cylinder. Figure 6.3.4 shows the top view with a front cross-sectional

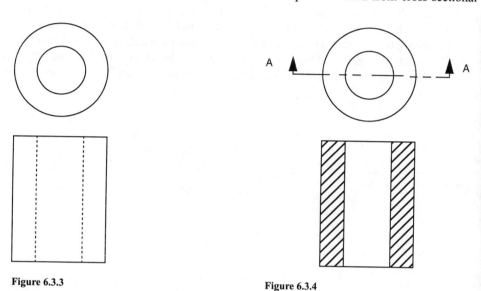

Figure 6.3.3   **Figure 6.3.4**

view. When constructing cross-sectional views, cutting-plane lines are added to the orthographic view adjacent to the sectional view. In this case, the cutting-plane line is visible in the top view and is labeled A-A. The arrows on the ends of a cutting-plane line indicate the direction from which one is viewing the object interior. In this figure, as indicated by the arrows at the ends of the cutting-plane line, the front half of the object has been removed, and one is viewing the back half. Note that after one has cut through the middle of the object, the lines once hidden (dashed) are now exposed and are therefore drawn as solid lines. Because the cutting plane was not passing through material in the hollowed out center of the cylinder, there is no cross-hatching shown for that part of the sectional view.

The cross-hatching used by engineers denotes that the cutting plane passes through material and signifies the material type for the part. Figure 6.3.5 shows some of the different types of cross-hatching used on engineering drawings and their corresponding material types.

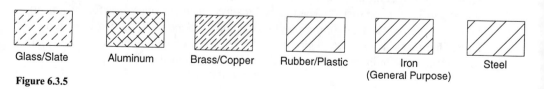

Glass/Slate   Aluminum   Brass/Copper   Rubber/Plastic   Iron   Steel
                                                                                    (General Purpose)

Figure 6.3.5

Full-sectional views occur when a cutting plane is passed through an entire object, exposing the interior. A half-sectional view can be used to show effectively both the interior and the exterior of an object. With a half-sectional view, the cutting plane cuts through only half of the object, and only the material in that half is removed. The drawing convention for this type of sectional view is that no hidden lines are shown for the entire object. Half-sectional views are typically used for objects with a generally cylindrical shape. Figure 6.3.6 shows a half-sectional view for an object.

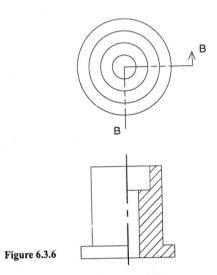

Figure 6.3.6

Note that for this half-sectional view, one-fourth of the object was removed. In the front view, the right half shows the interior of the object, while the left half shows the exterior. Neither side shows any hidden lines.

Highway Engineering

When engineers construct paved highways, they need to build a flat driving surface. The ground surface at a highway location generally is not flat; therefore, earth must be removed in some places and built up in others to achieve a flat highway surface. Once the earthwork is complete and a fairly level surface is obtained, pavement can be applied, resulting in a smooth driving surface.

Figure 6.3.7 shows a cross-section of the ground surface at a given location in a highway construction project. The desired finished road surface is superimposed on the drawing of the ground surface. The finished roadway includes sideslopes for the transition between pavement and existing ground on each side of the road. As can be seen in this figure, the material in the A region must be removed, or *cut*; whereas, the material in region B must be built up, or *filled*, to achieve the desired road grade.

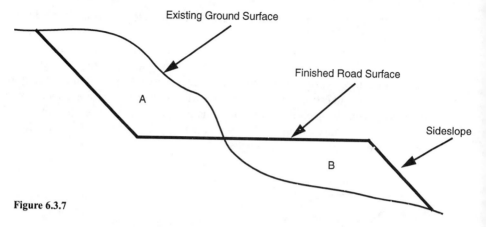

Figure 6.3.7

The engineer needs to know the volume of earthwork for a given construction project so that plans can be made for its successful completion. For example, if there is a great deal of excess cut material, the engineer must decide where to "waste" the excess. Conversely, if there is excess fill, a source for the extra material required must be determined. For designing the roadway, the engineer typically has cross-sectional views of the roadway at intervals of 50 to 100 feet. The volume of cut and the volume of fill between two cross sections is illustrated in Figure 6.3.8.

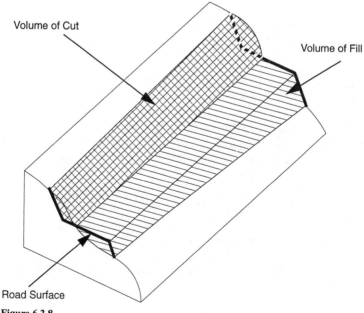

Figure 6.3.8

In this figure, the volume of cut between the two cross sections is labeled A, and the volume of fill is labeled B. To compute the volume of cut or fill, you first determine the approximate area of cut or fill at each cross section. For example, Figure 6.3.9 shows a cross-sectional view of the roadway drawn on square grid paper. In this example, to obtain the area of cut, each grid square represents 1 square foot. Count all of the full grid squares in the cut area, and estimate the area in the partial squares to arrive at an approximate area of cut for this cross section. Using the same procedure, determine the area of fill at this cross section. In this example, the approximate area of cut is 35 square feet, and the approximate area of fill is 25 square feet.

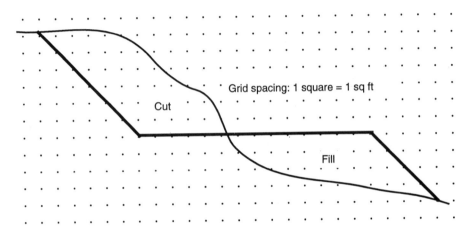

Figure 6.3.9

To obtain the volume of earthwork between two cross sections, compute the average area of cut and the average area of fill between the two sections, and multiply by the distance between them.

The cross-section shown in Figure 6.3.10 is located 100 feet away from the previous cross-section (shown in Figure 6.3.9). The approximate area of cut and fill at this cross-section are 15 square feet and 33 square feet, respectively. The volume of cut in this portion of the highway is therefore given as:

$$\text{Vol}_{\text{Cut}} = \left(\frac{35+15}{2}\right) \times 100 = 2500 \ \text{ft}^3 = \frac{2500}{27} = 93 \ \text{yd}^3$$

and the volume of fill in this section is given as:

$$\text{Vol}_{\text{Fill}} = \left(\frac{25+33}{2}\right) \times 100 = 2900 \ \text{ft}^3 = \frac{2900}{27} = 107 \ \text{yd}^3$$

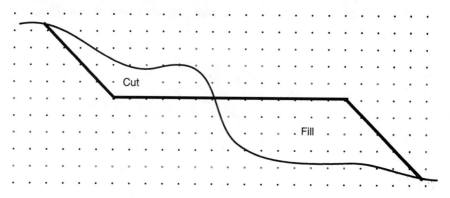

Figure 6.3.10

EXERCISES 6.3

1. Draw a vertical cross section of your bedroom.

2. Draw a floorplan of a possible first story of a house.

3. Draw a full front-sectional view for the object shown below.

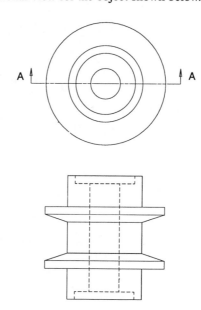

4. Draw a half-sectional view of the front view for the object shown below.

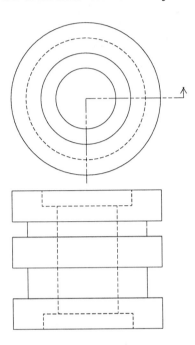

5. Draw a half-sectional view of the front view for the object shown below.

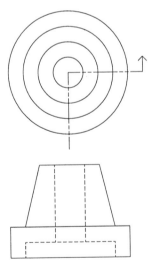

6. The distance between cross-section 1 and cross-section 2 shown below is 100 feet. Compute the volume of cut and the volume of fill for this section of highway.

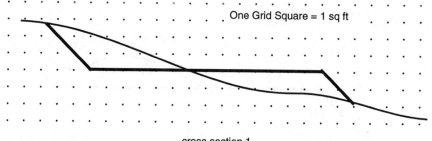

One Grid Square = 1 sq ft

cross section 1

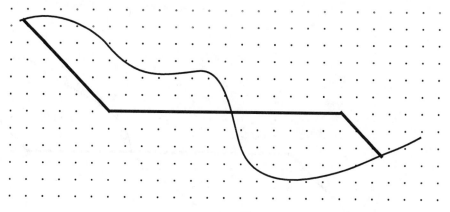

cross section 2

7. The distance between cross-section 1 and cross-section 2 shown below is 50 feet. Compute the volume of cut and the volume of fill for this section of highway.

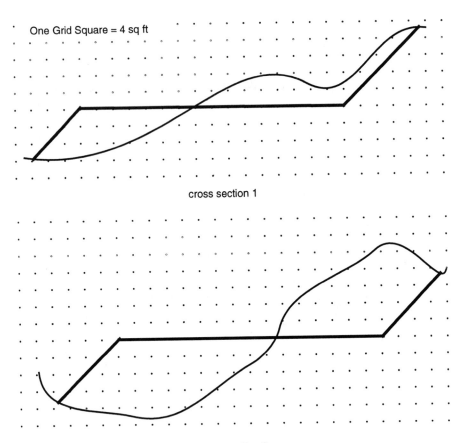

One Grid Square = 4 sq ft

cross section 1

cross section 2

7

Surfaces and Solids

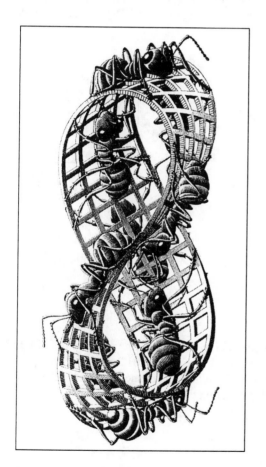

Mind teaser*: Are the ants crawling on the inside or on the outside of the surface?

Answer: On this surface, the inside and outside are the same. Surfaces of revolution, which will be studied in this chapter, however, have an inside and an outside.

The ability to imagine how a planar figure or region appears if rotated (or revolved) in various ways is a basic skill required of calculus students when they study surfaces and solids of revolution. Calculus students also must be able to visualize the curve formed by two intersecting surfaces or the volume common to two or more intersecting solids. Similar skills are required of engineering students when they design solid models of objects using computer aided design software. The following sections are designed to introduce you to these visualization skills and should benefit you in your later studies.

7.1 SURFACES OF REVOLUTION

If a planar figure is revolved (or rotated) about a coordinate axis or other line in 3-space, it generates a **surface of revolution**. The following two examples illustrate the use of line segments in forming surfaces of revolution.

    If the line segment $\overline{AB}$ with endpoints A(1, 2, 0) and B(4, 2, 0) is revolved about the X-axis, an open-ended cylinder is formed (see Figure 7.1.1). The cylinder has radius 2 and height 3, and is oriented along the X-axis.

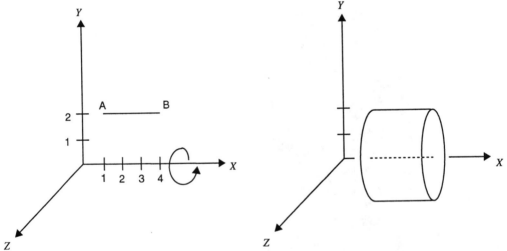

Figure 7.1.1

    The broken-line segments traced out by connecting the points A(0, 0, 0), B(2, 2, 0), C(2, 4, 0), and D(0, 4, 0) are shown at the left in Figure 7.1.2. If this broken-line segment is revolved about the Y-axis, a surface of revolution is formed that looks like a cone on the bottom half joined with a covered cylinder on the top half.

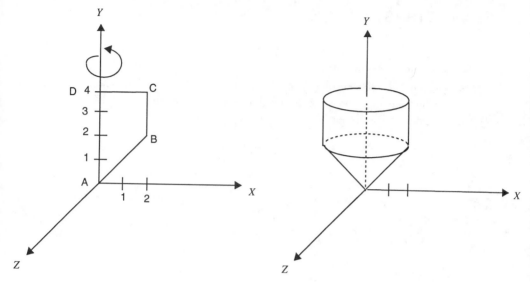

Figure 7.1.2

Figure 7.1.3a shows a circle graphed in the YZ-plane. If the circle is revolved about the Z-axis, the resulting surface of revolution is a sphere centered at $(0, 0, 2)$ with radius 1 (see Figure 7.1.3b). Whereas, if the circle is revolved about the Y-axis, the resulting surface is called a **torus**, which is a doughnut-shaped surface (see Figure 7.1.3c).

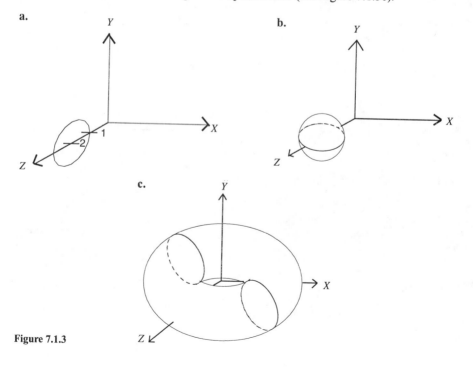

Figure 7.1.3

EXERCISES 7.1

1. Revolve the line segment $\overline{AB}$ with endpoints A(–2, 0, 0) and B(3, 5, 0) about the *Y*-axis. Draw and describe the surface of revolution.

2. A rectangle can be traced out by connecting the points shown below in the table. Sketch the rectangle on an *XYZ*-coordinate system and revolve it about the *X*-axis. Draw and describe the surface of revolution.

	Coordinates		
Point	*X*	*Y*	*Z*
A	1	1	0
B	1	3	0
C	5	3	0
D	5	1	0
A	1	1	0

3. A broken-line segment can be traced out by connecting the points A(0, 0, 0), B(1, 0, 0), C(2, 2, 0), D(1, 4, 0), and E(⅔, 5, 0). Sketch the line segment and revolve it about the *Y*-axis. Draw and describe the surface of revolution.

4. Below, a parabola is graphed in the *XZ*-plane. Draw the surface of revolution that results when the curve is revolved about the *Z*-axis. This surface is called a **paraboloid**.

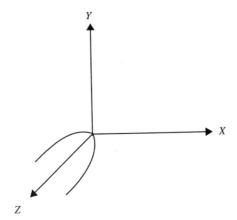

5. Below, a hyperbola is graphed in the *XY*-plane. Draw the surface of revolution that results when the hyperbola is revolved about the *X*-axis. This surface of revolution is called a **hyperboloid of two sheets**.

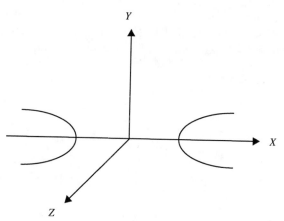

7.2 SOLIDS OF REVOLUTION

A **solid of revolution** is generated when a planar region is revolved about a coordinate axis or some other line in 3-space. Whereas a surface of revolution is like a hollow shell, a solid of revolution has mass inside and is usually shaded to indicate that it is dense throughout its volume. Figure 7.2.1 shows the visual distinction between a cylinder that is a surface of revolution formed by revolving a vertical line about the Y-axis (Figure 7.2.1a) and a cylinder that is a solid of revolution formed by revolving a rectangular region about the Y-axis (Figure 7.2.1b).

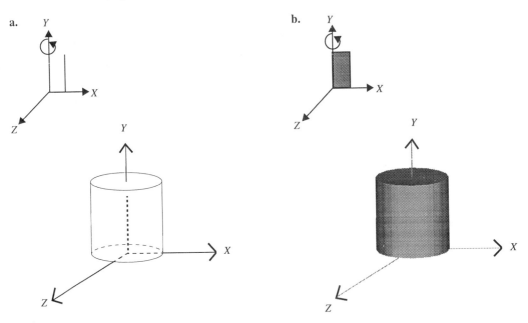

Figure 7.2.1

The statement that a solid of revolution is dense throughout its volume does not mean that solids of revolution cannot have some open space in their interiors. For example, if the rectangular region shown in Figure 7.2.2a is revolved about the Y-axis, a solid of revolution is formed (Figure 7.2.2b) that looks like a solid cylinder with a cylindrical hole bored through its center.

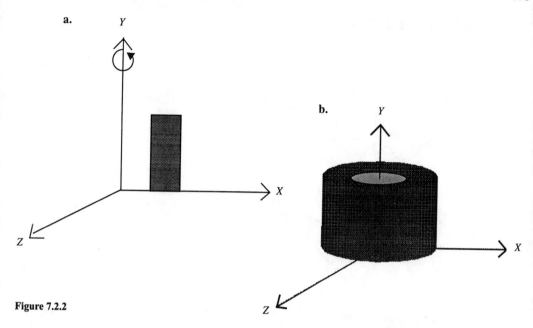

Figure 7.2.2

If the semicircular region shown in Figure 7.2.3a is revolved about the X-axis, a **ball** (or solid sphere) of radius 2 centered at the origin is the solid of revolution formed (see Figure 7.2.3b).

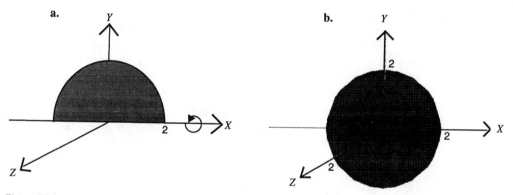

Figure 7.2.3

EXERCISES 7.2

1. Revolve the triangular region shown below about the Z-axis. Draw and name the solid of revolution.

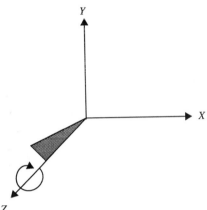

2. The drawing below shows a region bounded above by half of an ellipse and below by the X-axis. Revolve the region about the X-axis and draw the solid of revolution. It is called an **ellipsoid**. What is the intersection of the plane $x = 4$ and the ellipsoid? (*Note:* If you do not use dark shading, be sure to include this cross section to give the ellipsoid a 3-D appearance.)

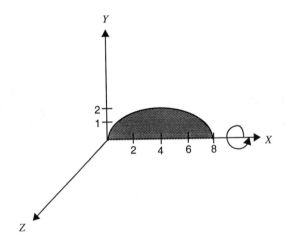

3. Revolve the section of a circular region shown below about the *Y*-axis. Draw and describe the solid of revolution.

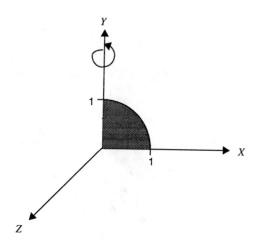

4. Revolve the rectangular region shown below about the *X*-axis. Draw and describe the solid of revolution.

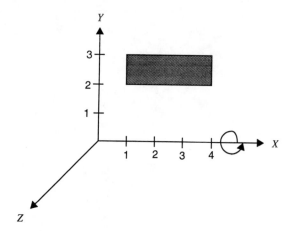

5. Revolve the triangular region shown below about the Z-axis. This planar region lies in
   the XZ-plane. Draw and describe the solid of revolution.

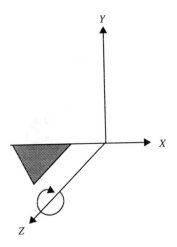

7.3 COMBINING SOLIDS

Visualizing the combination of two or more solids can be a nontrivial task; however, we will limit this discussion to fairly simple situations. Graphics software can be an invaluable tool in more complicated situations.

The goal of combining two solids may differ from one situation to another. Figure 7.3.1 shows some possible results from combining a block and a cylinder. Figure 7.3.1a shows a block and a cylinder joined to make a more complicated solid. Figure 7.3.1b shows a block with a cylinder cut out of its center to create a block with a hole in it. Figure 7.3.1c shows the common volume shared by the intersection of the block and cylinder (i.e., a cylinder the same height as the block).

a.   b.   c.

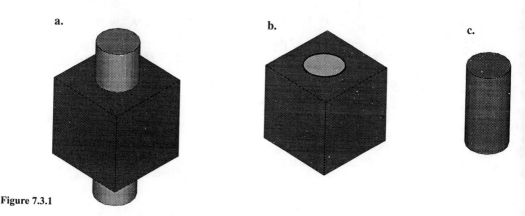

Figure 7.3.1

In calculus, students learn how to set up integrals to solve for the volume of a *trapped solid*. Imagine two cylinders intersecting at right angles. A solid will be trapped inside these two intersecting cylinders by the sides of the cylinders even though the cylinders themselves may be open-ended. If we let one cylinder open in the X-direction and the other in the Y-direction, then the volume of the trapped solid is equally distributed across the eight octants. The easiest way to solve this problem is to visualize the solid formed by the intersection of the cylinders in Octant I, set up the integrals to solve for its volume, and multiply by 8 to get the final answer. Figure 7.3.2 shows an isometric view of the part of the trapped solid that is located in Octant I. Note that the part of each cylinder in Octant I is one-fourth of the full cylinder. The shaded part in Figure 7.3.2 is one-eighth of the whole trapped solid.

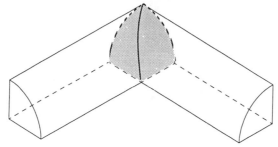

Figure 7.3.2

Figure 7.3.3 shows what remains of a cylinder after a right circular cone is cut from its center. The same resulting solid can be generated by revolving the triangle shown in Figure 7.3.4 about the Y-axis. When engineers create solid objects utilizing computer aided design software, they must decide which of these two approaches is easier: (1) modifying a common solid such as a block, cylinder, cone, or sphere, or (2) drawing a **profile** (or cross section) and revolving it about an axis or other line.

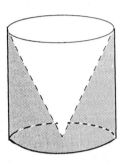

Figure 7.3.3

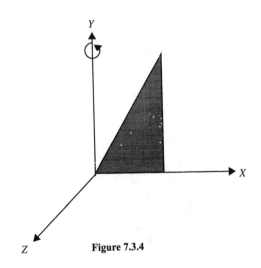

Figure 7.3.4

EXERCISES 7.3

In Exercises 1 to 4, describe how to create the pictured solid by combining two or more common solids. Common solids are defined here to mean cones, cylinders, cubes, and spheres. Combining two solids here should be for the purpose of joining two solids or for cutting one solid from another.

1.

2.

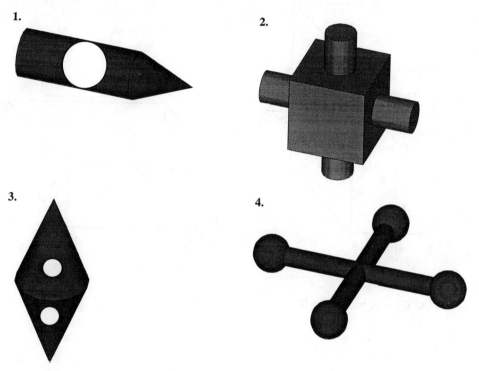

3.

4.

In Exercises 5 and 6, draw the trapped solid formed by intersecting the two given solids. Draw each trapped solid to scale on an *XYZ*-coordinate system and shade it lightly.

5. Rectangular prism A and rectangular prism B

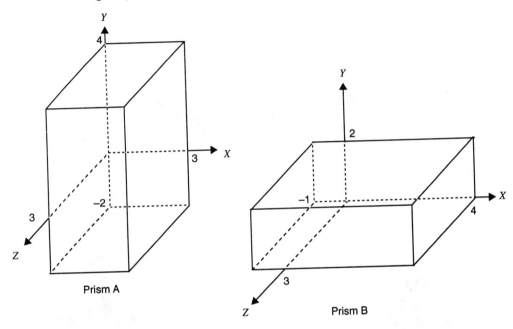

6. Cone A and sphere B

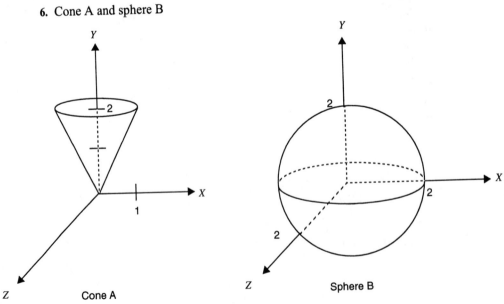

7.4 APPLICATIONS

Turning

After an engineer has designed a part for use in a final product, it is up to machinists to create a prototype and then to mass-produce the part. There are many methods of manufacture and many different types of tools available. One of the most useful machine tools is called a *lathe*. A lathe is capable of performing many different functions within a machine shop, from drilling holes and adding threads to turning parts. We will focus on turning in this section.

A lathe is used for turning parts that are generally cylindrical in nature. Figure 7.4.1 shows a basic schematic of a lathe and illustrates the principle involved in turning a part. In **turning**, the original piece of material is placed in the lathe and rotated continuously about the long axis of the lathe. The speed of rotation depends on the material of the part. The cutting tool is set to a specified cutting depth, and material along the outer surface of the part is removed. As the part is rotated, the cutting tool moves along the axis of rotation, and the depth of the cut may be varied accordingly. Thus, turning is used to create a surface of revolution on the outer surface of a part.

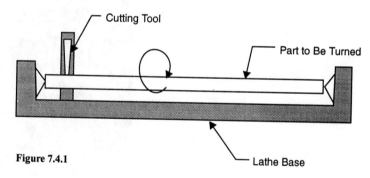

Figure 7.4.1

For metal parts, turning is usually done either to a constant or to a tapered diameter. Large changes in diameter are turned by physically moving the cutting tool from one section of the part to another and adjusting the cutting depth. For wooden parts, a larger degree of variation in cutting depths is possible because the material is "softer." For example, wooden spindles on chair backs or table legs are produced by turning wood in a lathe.

Computer-Aided Design

Engineers use computers to design, analyze, and manufacture many types of objects. There are many different methods available in the creation of objects using design software. Once an object has been created, its geometry can be transferred to an analysis program for testing. For example, a part can be analyzed by a method known as *finite element analysis* to determine areas of high stress or temperature on complex parts. Once the part has been analyzed on the computer screen, the design can be modified and then reanalyzed. After an optimum design is established, the object geometry can be sent to another software package to set up cutting tool paths for part production. With the use of computer software, one can take an idea from a concept in a designer's imagination to a working physical part.

In computer-aided design, the creation of the solid geometry is the basis for the entire design procedure. To set up computer models for analysis and manufacture, it is first necessary to create the 3-D object using the software. There are many methods of creation available to the engineer. Simple objects such as blocks and cylinders can be created directly, planar profiles can be extruded, planar profiles can be revolved, or two objects may be combined (by either adding, subtracting, or intersecting) to form a third object.

Revolution of a planar profile to sweep a solid object is commonly used in the creation of objects that are generally cylindrical in shape. Just as mathematicians sweep the equation of a parabola to form a paraboloid, engineered parts can be created by revolving a profile to form a desired solid object. Figure 7.4.2 shows a profile to be revolved in engineering design software.

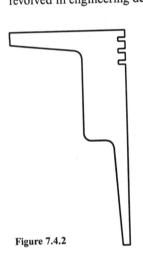

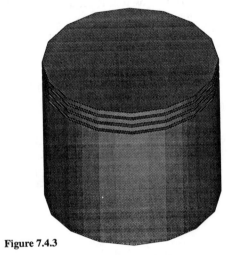

Figure 7.4.2   **Figure 7.4.3**

The object obtained from revolving this profile is a piston. Revolving the profile creates the solid object shown in Figure 7.4.3. Figure 7.4.4 shows the profile revolved about the X-axis to create the pulley in Figure 7.4.5.

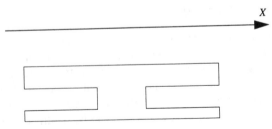

Figure 7.4.4

Pulley Shown with Part Cut Away   Entire Pulley

Figure 7.4.5

Another method of object creation in computer-aided design is profile extrusion. By this method, a 2-D profile is extruded or "pushed back" a specified distance. Extrusion is a manufacturing process in which material is forced through an opening and the resulting product takes on the cross section of the opening. A Play-Doh Fun Factory®, a child's toy, demonstrates the principle of extrusion. In essence, when a profile is extruded on the computer screen, the original profile remains in position, an exact copy of the profile is located a specified distance away from the original, and the endpoints of all lines and curves from the original to the copy are included to define the solid object. Figure 7.4.6 shows a profile and the resulting 3-D object created by extrusion.

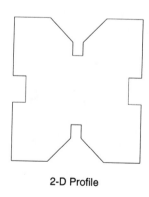

2-D Profile

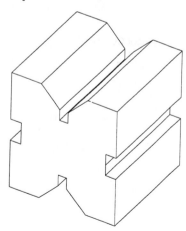

Figure 7.4.6   3-D Object from Extrusion

   The third primary method for object creation in computer-aided design is to combine
the geometry of two objects by cutting, joining, or intersecting volumes. This results in a
third object distinctly different from the original two objects but also similar to them. For
example, Figure 7.4.7 shows a block and a cylinder. Also shown in this figure are the
resulting objects obtained from the cylinder cutting the block, the block cutting the cylinder,
the block and cylinder joined together and intersection of the block and the cylinder.

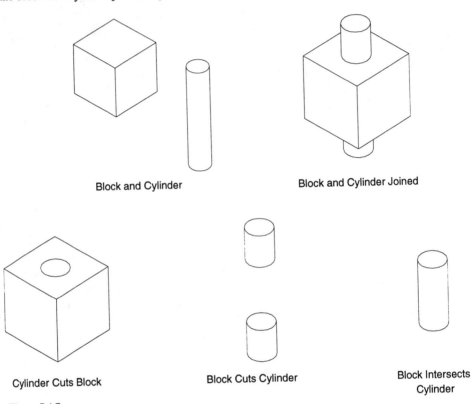

Block and Cylinder   Block and Cylinder Joined

Cylinder Cuts Block   Block Cuts Cylinder   Block Intersects
                                                          Cylinder

Figure 7.4.7

Most "real-life" objects can be created by a combination of these modeling techniques. For example, the object shown in Figure 7.4.8 is created by a combination of extrusion and cutting and joining primitive shapes. Figure 7.4.9 shows the series of steps used to produce this object.

Figure 7.4.8

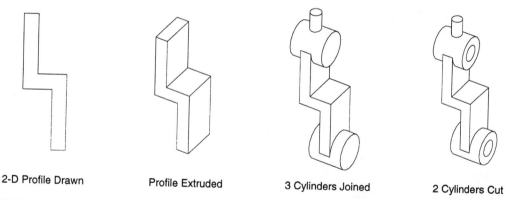

2-D Profile Drawn   Profile Extruded   3 Cylinders Joined   2 Cylinders Cut

Figure 7.4.9

If you are an engineer who needs to create 3-D objects using computer-aided design methods, it is important that you are able to break down an object's geometry into the individual pieces from which it is made. Often, an object can be created in more than one way. How would you go about creating the object shown in Figure 7.4.10?

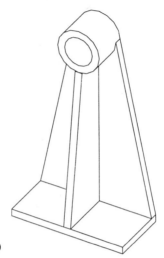

Figure 7.4.10

Two possible methods for creating this object are shown in Figures 7.4.11 and 7.4.12.

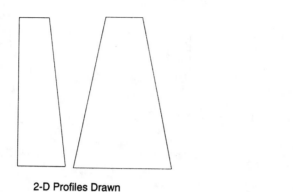

2-D Profiles Drawn

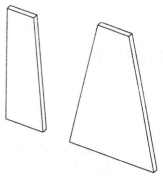

Profiles Extruded

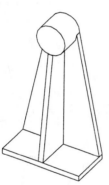

Extruded Objects, One
Block and One Cylinder
Figure 7.4.11   Joined

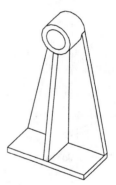

Cylinder Cut Through Object

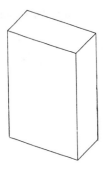

Block Created

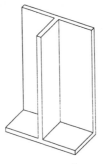

Two Blocks Cut

Four Blocks Cut

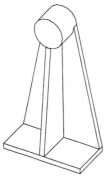

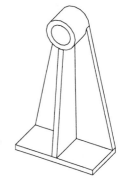

Figure 7.4.12   Cylinder Joined

Cylinder Cut Through Object

EXERCISES 7.4

1. Sketch a curve that could be used in turning a spindle for an antique chair back shown in the figure below.

2. Sketch a profile that could be used in computer-aided design to create a rocket.

3. Sketch a profile that could be used to create a pop bottle by revolution.

4. Sketch a profile that could be used to create a machine screw by revolution.

5. Sketch a profile that could be used to create a tire and rim by revolution.

6. Sketch the procedure you would use to create the object shown below by computer-aided design methods.

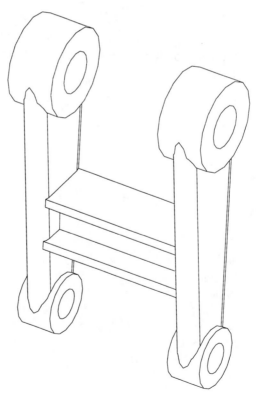

7. Sketch the procedure you would use to create the object shown below by computer-aided design methods.

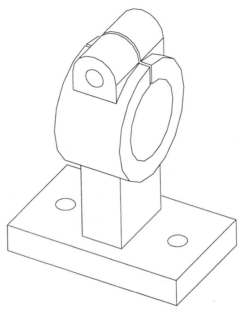

8. Sketch the procedure you would use to create the object shown below by computer-aided design methods.

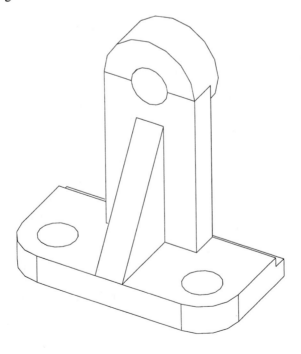

9. Sketch the procedure you would use to create the object shown below by computer-aided design methods.

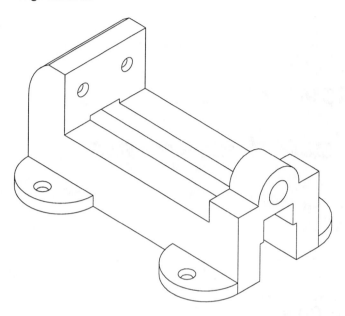

Appendix I

Answers to
Selected Exercises

CHAPTER 1

EXERCISES 1.1

2. Careers that would not require spatial visualization ability: accountants, bankers, clerks, data entry personnel, IRS workers, receptionists, stockbrokers, and models.

EXERCISES 1.2

2. Topological activities: playing with Silly Putty™, with rubber bands, sports with balls, cutting and folding paper.
Projective activities: playing Tetris™, playing with blocks, drawing corner views.
Euclidean activities: visualizing water heights as the container is tilted, expanding objects, rotating objects.
3. Visualizing such things as distance, area, and volume is difficult because we are accustomed to measuring or calculating these things. Further, in most career areas, it is sufficient to be able to measure and calculate these things.

EXERCISES 1.3

1. C

3. C

5.

8.

9. B

11. A

13. D

15. B

CHAPTER 2

EXERCISES 2.1

1.

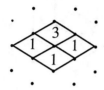

3.

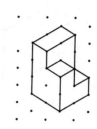

5.

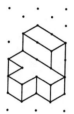

7.

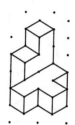

9.

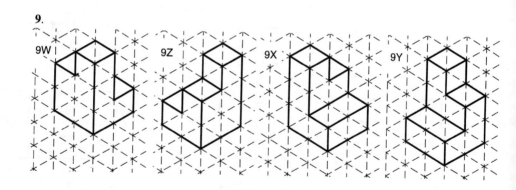

11.

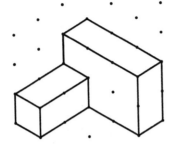

14.

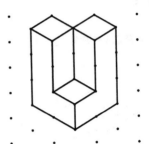

16.

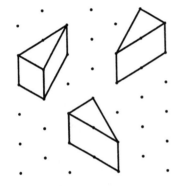

EXERCISES 2.2

1.

3.

5.

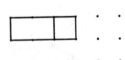

7.

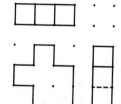

9.

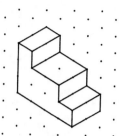

11.

13.

15.

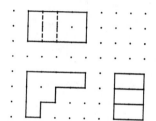

EXERCISES 2.3

1.

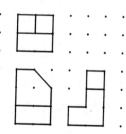

3.

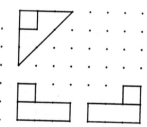

5.

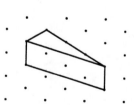

7.

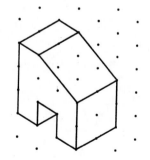

EXERCISES 2.4

1.

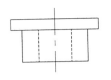

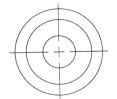

5.

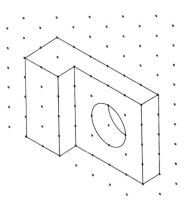

7.

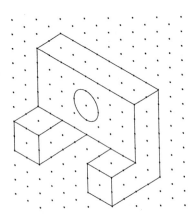

9.

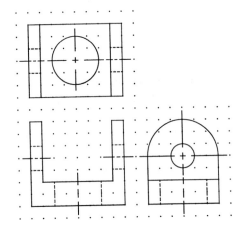

EXERCISES 2.5

2.

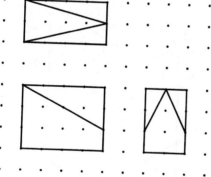

4.

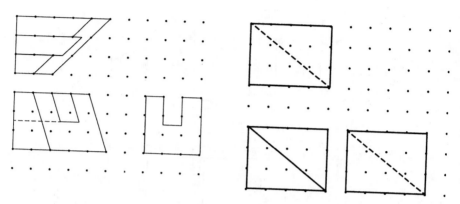

6.

EXERCISES 2.6

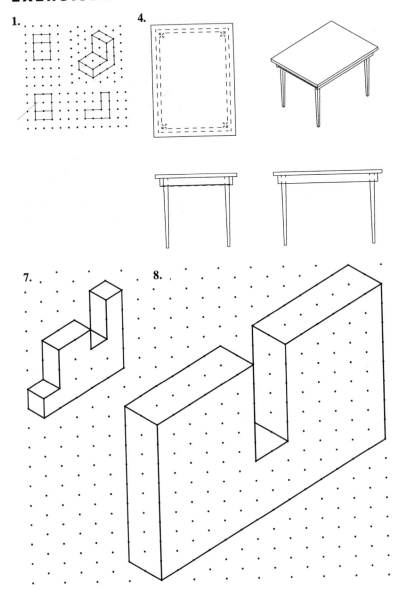

1.

4.

7.

8.

CHAPTER 3

EXERCISES 3.1

1.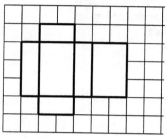

3.

5. A

7. D

EXERCISES 3.2

1.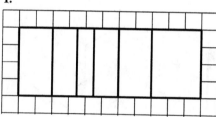

4.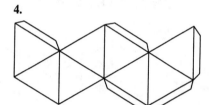

7.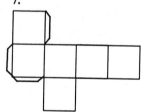

8.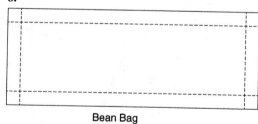

Bean Bag

CHAPTER 4

EXERCISES 4.1

2.

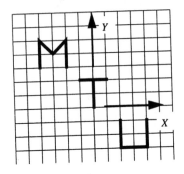

EXERCISES 4.2

1. Oblique, right-handed
3. Isometric, left-handed
5. Z-axis

EXERCISES 4.3

3.

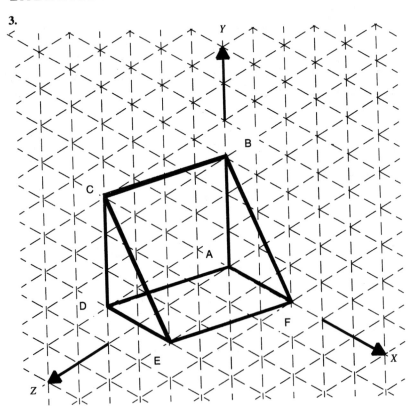

EXERCISES 4.4

1.

Line	Departure +East	Departure −West	Latitude +North	Latitude −South
AB	184.0		188.5	
BC	201.2			107.0
CD	119.7		169.0	
DE	106.9			507.3
EA		611.8	256.6	

Coordinates	X	Y
A	0	0
B	184.0	188.5
C	385.2	81.5
D	504.9	250.5
E	611.8	−256.7
A	0	0

CHAPTER 5

EXERCISES 5.1

1.

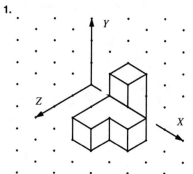

3.

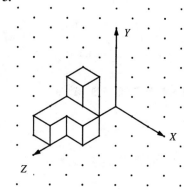

5.

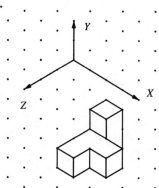

9.

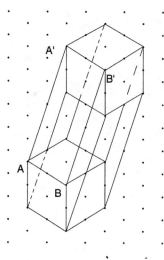

7. (−4, 0, 2)

EXERCISES 5.2

2.

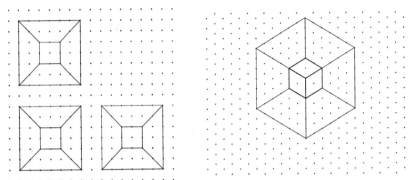

It is difficult because the smaller cube looks as if it is located in the far corner of the larger cube rather than floating in the center of the larger cube.

3. Drawing an object to scale is not a transformation because the actual lengths of the sides do not change.

4. 21 inches or 54 centimeters

6. 1:63360

7. A 4-inch line should be drawn.

EXERCISES 5.3

1.

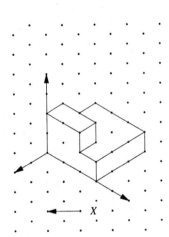

2.

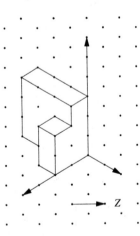

5.

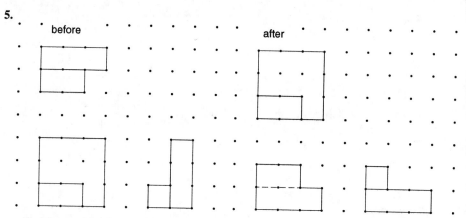

The views are different.

7. The object was rotated –90° about the *Y*-axis. ⟶ *Y*
9. Equal (=)
11. Equal (=)

EXERCISES 5.4

3.

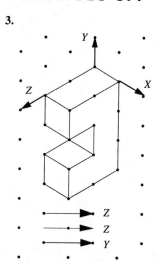

4.

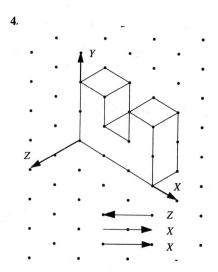

5.

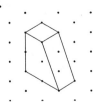

7.

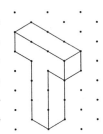

9.

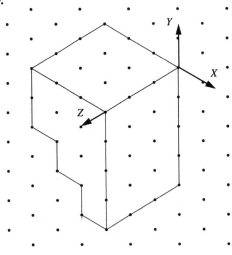

EXERCISES 5.5

1.

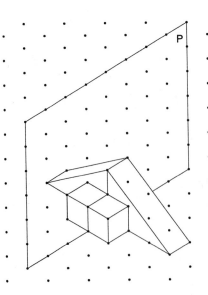

3.

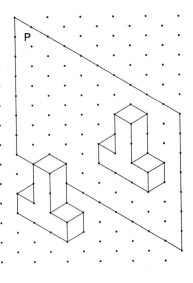

5. Two planes of symmetry
7. Yes, two 90° will work.

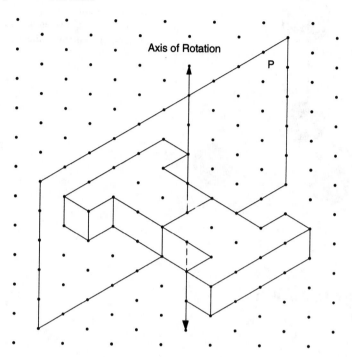

EXERCISES 5.6

1.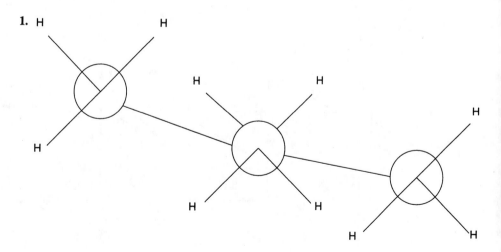

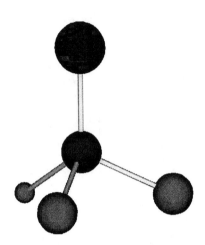

2b. No

2c. It is optically active; it will rotate plane-polarized light when passed through a solution containing the isomer.

CHAPTER 6

EXERCISES 6.1

2a.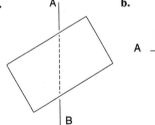

b.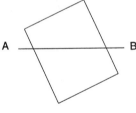

c.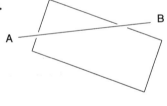

4.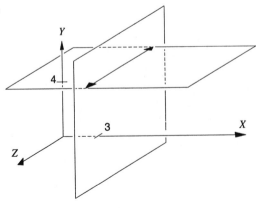

6.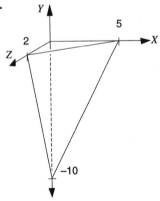

7.

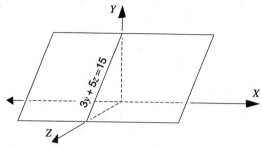

EXERCISES 6.2

2. A point and a parabola

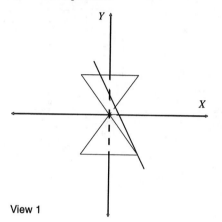

View 1

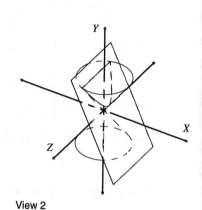

View 2

3.

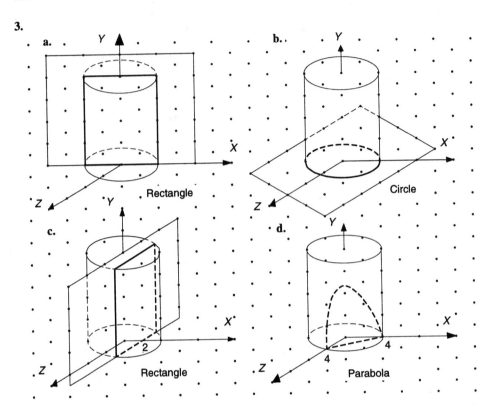

EXERCISES 6.3

1.

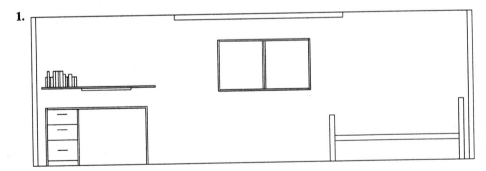

3.

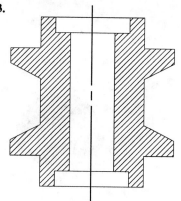

5.

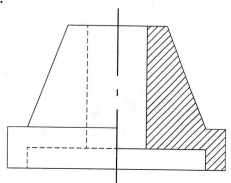

CHAPTER 7

EXERCISES 7.1

1. Double cone

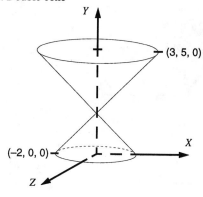

5.

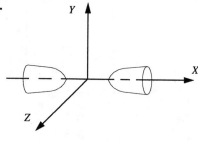

3.

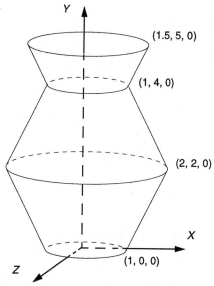

EXERCISES 7.2

1. cone

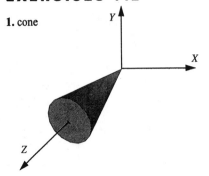

3. hemisphere

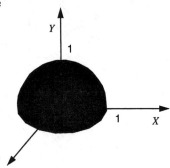

EXERCISES 7.3

2. Start with a cube. Join a vertical cylinder to the cube through its center. Then join a horizontal cylinder to the cube through its center.

3. Join two right cones at their bases. Cut each cone with a small cylinder.

6.

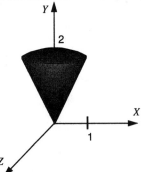

EXERCISES 7.4

1.

3.

5.

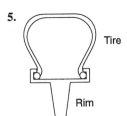

Tire

Rim

Appendix II

Paper Supplies

1 cm Square Grid Paper

2 cm Square Grid Paper

Square Grid Paper

Square Dot Paper

Isometric Grid Paper

Isometric Dot Paper (Large Spacing)

Isometric Dot Paper (Small Spacing)

Engineering Drawing Layout Paper

One Centimeter Grid Paper

Two Centimeter Grid Paper

Square Grid Paper

Square Dot Paper

Isometric Grid Paper

Isometric Dot Paper (Large Spacing)

Isometric Dot Paper (Small Spacing)

Engineering Drawing Layout Paper

Index